This book is due for return on or before the last date
shown above but it may be renewed by personal
application, post, or telephone, quoting this date and
the book number.

HERTFORDSHIRE COUNTY LIBRARY
COUNTY HALL, HERTFORD.

L.32

WITHDRAWN

FACTORY LAY-OUT
PLANNING AND PROGRESS

FACTORY LAY-OUT PLANNING & PROGRESS

WITH SPECIAL REFERENCE TO ENGINEERING

BY

W. J. HISCOX

AUTHOR OF "FACTORY ADMINISTRATION IN PRACTICE"

FOURTH EDITION BY

JAMES STIRLING

ASSOCIATE MEMBER, THE INSTITUTION OF MECHANICAL
ENGINEERS

LONDON
SIR ISAAC PITMAN & SONS LTD.

First edition 1929
Second edition 1935
Reprinted 1939, 1941
Third edition 1943
Reprinted 1944, 1946
Fourth edition 1948
Reprinted 1958, 1960, 1963

SIR ISAAC PITMAN & SONS Ltd.
PITMAN HOUSE, PARKER STREET, KINGSWAY, LONDON, W.C.2
THE PITMAN PRESS, BATH
PITMAN HOUSE, BOUVERIE STREET, CARLTON, MELBOURNE
22–25 BECKETT'S BUILDINGS, PRESIDENT STREET, JOHANNESBURG

ASSOCIATED COMPANIES
PITMAN MEDICAL PUBLISHING COMPANY Ltd.
46 CHARLOTTE STREET, LONDON, W.1

PITMAN PUBLISHING CORPORATION
20 EAST 46TH STREET, NEW YORK 17, NEW YORK

SIR ISAAC PITMAN & SONS (CANADA) Ltd.
(INCORPORATING THE COMMERCIAL TEXT BOOK COMPANY
PITMAN HOUSE, 381–383 CHURCH STREET, TORONTO

MADE IN GREAT BRITAIN AT THE PITMAN PRESS, BATH
F3—(B.1794)

PREFACE TO THE FIRST EDITION

THE author endeavours in this work to portray the ethics of factory planning as understood by a man who for many years has been brought into daily contact with the manifold problems arising out of modern industrial conditions.

It is not the work of an "expert," for the word implies the maximum of proficiency, a degree unattained by mortal man, but it is the work of a specialist—a persistent seeker after the truth. The industrial book must portray the views of its author, and those views are necessarily based upon his experience of, and his association with, industry. Each writer has one main theme, to which all others are subservient, and thus we find the University graduate discussing economics and psychology, the cost accountant charges and expenses, and the shopman managerial problems.

The development of the principal theme, in its relation to industrial efficiency, renders necessary the exposition of a scheme of workshop organization, and in the present work the scheme is unfolded in a non-technical manner, with a view to ensuring easy reading. The author's arguments are based upon a sublime belief in British ingenuity and common sense, and upon the belief that the British manufacturer can, by his own judgment and his own sagacity, regain that which he has allowed to go astray.

The difficulties of the factory are often rendered formidable by the timorous attitude of some directorates, who would rather temporize than plunge. They fear to trust their factory officials—those experienced men who know what is wanted, and who know how to get it—and adopt instead a vacillating policy that makes no progress. In matters affecting factory management and organization the shopman can see a good deal farther than the director, and if he is given the necessary facilities he will make short work of difficulties.

Whilst hoping to attract the "big stars," the author will be disappointed if this work fails to engage the attention of the "lesser lights of the industrial firmament"—those ambitious young fellows who will one day be heads of departments, and probably factory managers. It is, unfortunately, the case that many of them do not

v

seem to appreciate industrial literature, and it would seem that the higher officials make no effort to foster their interest. In the interest of industrial efficiency and individual proficiency this must not be allowed to continue, for broadmindedness is essential even to the specialist, who must have some knowledge of the phases adjacent to his own preserve in order to gain a high degree of proficiency.

The first work[1] of the author gave unusual prominence to the "progress system" as the basis of factory administration, and in the present volume will be found a treatise on "Progress Work," which it is hoped will prove of interest to every member of the executive staff, from the works manager downwards. The instances given cater for practically every circumstance likely to arise in any manufacturing concern, and the "what to do" is in every case based on "what has been done."

W. J. H.

PREFACE TO LATER EDITIONS

In preparing further editions of this work by the late Mr. W. J. Hiscox, the writer has endeavoured to extend its usefulness to advanced students of the subjects covered. Additional subject matter includes consideration of the lay-out of plant for continuous process manufacture and of the systematization of procedure for controlled alterations to standard products. The Drawing Office function is outlined and several sections, that on Rate-fixing for example, have been amplified.

It is believed that the work is particularly suitable for those preparing for such professional examinations as the final of The Institute of Cost and Works Accountants.

JAMES STIRLING.

[1] *Factory Administration in Practice* (Pitman).

CONTENTS

CHARTS AND DIAGRAMS

PART I—PLANNING AND ROUTEING

CHAPTER I

FACTORY PLANNING—AND WHAT IS INVOLVED

THE art of planning a factory is not easily acquired, and it is to be feared that it is not assiduously sought. We hear a great deal concerning the planning activities of well-organized concerns, but when these activities are analysed we find that the spasmodic element prevails—spasmodic in the sense that the matter is handled piecemeal, a bit here and a bit there, as an opening occurs. In most factories the reason is obvious, for the factory was in existence and the system established long before the advent of the planner, who came upon the scene when the factory was a hive of industry and when the fundamentals of the system were too firmly rooted to permit of transplanting.

We find that the advent of the planner coincides with the establishment of a bonus system, and that his activities are limited to the standardizing of operations and rates. He may in some instances effect reforms in the lay-out of the plant for the purpose of facilitating production, by re-grouping machines, devising more up-to-date accessories, and superseding certain units by more modern appliances. He may institute a more efficient method of transport, revolutionize by means of operation planning the grade of labour, and exploit the advantages he has created by means of co-ordination in the matter of routine. These reforms are undoubtedly valuable, and entitle the management to boast of their well-organized factory, but the scope of the planner is limited nevertheless. He works upon what is already in existence—the construction of the factory, its floor area, the design of the product, and the policy of the directors, as exemplified by the system prevailing.

It may be said that this is wholly attributable to the fact already mentioned—that when the planner enters the factory the system is already in existence, and as a consequence it is impossible for these matters to be handled by him. He cannot raze the building to the ground and erect another to his own specification, neither can he remove the factory to a more satisfactory site. And bearing in mind that planning is a comparatively modern institution, it is obvious that the majority of the factories in this country were built and equipped long before the cult of factory planning became popular.

These objections may be accepted for the moment, although they will again be referred to. Just now, however, it is proposed to deal briefly with the newly established workshop, and endeavour to discover if factory planning is on a higher plane here.

Frankly speaking, it is not, according to the observations of the writer. There are new factories where planning is a prominent feature, just as there are old ones, but it is not possible to assert that the organization of the new factory is superior to that of the old, simply because it is of more modern construction. One will find the same methods in both factories—the principle of planning is accepted, but it is introduced after the system has become established, and after the equipment has been installed. It does not appear to be recognized that planning must precede these moves in order to control them. There are exceptions, of course, but the number is small, and even here there is evidence that the planning has not been wholly successful. A foundry was carefully planned and equipped, and it seemed as though every contingency had been provided against—until inquiries began to pour in. Then it was discovered that the type of product for which there was a market could not be handled economically without drastic changes, involving a good deal of time and expense. The planning was too narrow, and there had been too much assumption. It was based on the belief that the machine could handle any moulding within certain dimensions, but practice showed it could not.

Most firms start off in too much of a hurry. They have a commodity which they know (or imagine) will command a market, and they are eager to get it placed. It is estimated that the yearly sales will reach a certain figure, and that for manufacture a certain floor area is necessary. A factory which conforms more or less to the requirement is built, bought or rented, and this is equipped with power machinery of a standard range, such as lathes, millers, grinders, drillers, and the like. It may be considered necessary in some instances to install modern equipment, whilst in others a cheaper type of machine may be favoured, but for what precise purpose each is intended cannot be ascertained at the moment. It is expected that, as time goes on, the various units will "shave themselves down" and the factory will find its own level.

The location of departments for handling the various stages of manufacture is conducted in the same haphazard fashion, and two or three changes will probably have to be made before the ideal lay-out is found. The works manager and his assistants are appointed after the system has been formulated and the equipment installed, which means that, instead of the works manager being responsible for the carrying out of the policy of the directors, and using his discretion in the matter of detail, he is compelled to work in accordance with a system which restricts the scope of his activities. It is significant that, in the early years of the new factory's existence, changes in the higher command are frequent, and it is extremely rare to find, at the end of ten or twelve years, the same individual occupying the managerial chair who occupied it when the factory came into existence.

In the engagement of labour the easiest line of resistance is followed, the policy being to man the machines, and have a sorting out afterwards. This obviously has the effect of increasing the labour turnover, but it also has the effect of establishing the "inefficient indispensable," the man who, by good fortune or by influence, manages to retain his footing, and in course of time to become a kind of "oracle" simply because he is an old servant.

The design of each component part of the unit is settled long before manufacture commences, but real working drawings are conspicuous by their absence. There are, maybe, drawings upon which are crowded the outlines of a dozen different parts, and from these the various foremen get to know what the parts should look like. In these circumstances, standardized operations cannot be devised, and a bonus system of payment is quite out of the question. Economical manufacture is impossible, but it *is* possible to go ahead, and for the moment nothing else matters.

This is the policy which governs the start up of many factories at the present time, when older factories are endeavouring to minimize the effects of early sins by means of reorganization. Why should the youth of an enlightened age copy the early mistakes of his grandfather, who is doing all he can to rectify them? Surely it is up to the youth to start off from at least that level which, after much struggling, the old man has attained, rather than to fall to the bottom of the pit, and commence an upward struggle on his own account.

Yet this is continually happening in industry, and will happen whilst planning is left until a favourable opportunity occurs, which is usually when things begin to go wrong. There is no excuse for the new factory if it does not immediately take its place by the side of older established concerns, for it has undeniable advantages in being born in the days of specialization, and having at its disposal the services of the expert.

The older established concern must needs be improved as and when the opportunity occurs, but even here, in many instances, *the* opportunity is not always seized. As before suggested, the favourable opportunity is represented as being the time when things begin to go wrong, but really this is an unsafe dictum to follow. When the management realizes that things are beginning to go wrong, it may be taken for granted that things are very wrong indeed, and the task of reorganization will be a protracted one. The average works manager is the last man to detect signs of a "rot"—the "rot" will have taken a firm hold long before he recognizes its presence. "Things are going on very well," thinks he, because there is no definite sign of their being otherwise, but the newcomer to the factory knows differently, and so do the factory officials of a lower grade, who are up against trouble daily.

Some years ago a number of enlightened factory officials (heads of departments and the like) were convinced that all was not well with the factory, and voiced their fears to the higher management. The concern was apparently well-established, and had been in existence many years—it seemed presumptuous, therefore, for a number of minor officials (many of them comparative newcomers) to tell the management of a flourishing concern that their policy was wrong; and, as may be expected, the presumptuous ones were quietly but firmly "put back into their places" by the higher authorities. Time went on—the concern continued to flourish (in the eyes of the management), but the malcontents were still apprehensive, and after much thought they again decided to approach the management. This time they determined to be more explicit, and drafted out a report, showing what in their opinion was wrong and how it could be remedied. Their representations, however, met with no better success than formerly, but so convinced were they of the danger that threatened, that they became seriously alarmed, and in a few weeks many had quitted the factory and sought safety elsewhere. In six months the management saw that "things were beginning to go wrong," and sought to remedy the trouble by adopting the methods advocated, but the matter had gone too far for these methods to be successful, and yet the management would not resort to more drastic measures. Within twelve months the fears of those who knew were realized, and those who had taken precautions to render themselves safe had reason to congratulate themselves upon their astuteness, for the erstwhile flourishing factory could not continue the fight, and the gates were closed.

This is but one instance of an unrecognized opportunity, but it will serve to show that "when things begin to go wrong" is not the time for initial action. It is true that any time is the time for action, but it is true also that the longer action is delayed the more drastic it must be to achieve the desired result. Many concerns to-day are in a bad way, and this is recognized by the management. Others are not so bad, and it is here that the remedy can be applied, if the management will exaggerate instead of minimize the apparent danger, and take immediate steps to combat it. If they will not do so, they are only intensifying trouble in the future, which will either bring about a crash, or necessitate drastic action, the expense of which will cripple the resources of the concern for a decade.

It is time now for the management of every manufacturing concern to review the organization of the factory from the standpoint of planning, even though this factor is already recognized by means of a planning department. If the matter has proceeded so far, an analysis of the functions of the department will in all probability show that its scope can be considerably extended. If, on the other hand, planning has not received official recognition, it is time that it did so, but at the same time it must be borne in mind that it exists to a certain degree in some guise.

In the older-established factory matters have obviously gone too far to allow planning the fullest scope, for the building has been constructed and equipped. Even in this connection, however, a fair amount of latitude may be allowed, notably as regards extensions to the building and lay-out adjustments. No firm carries on manufacture for a great number of years without making some change in the design of the product, and in most factories somewhat extensive changes are made at least every three or four years, in order to bring the product up to date. It is when one of these changes is imminent that the time is ripe for action, for the product can be planned from source to finish. In this case the design can be made to conform with the equipment existing, with such adjustments as may be deemed necessary in the light of practical experience, such as the provision of one or two up-to-date machines, jigs, and tools, etc., the latter being determined through the medium of operation planning.

A good beginning does not necessarily ensure continual efficiency, but it is a vital matter, nevertheless. It is said that the dustman would make as good a Prime Minister as the duke, given the same opportunities, but it is at once apparent that the former would be severely handicapped, and would have to work considerably harder than the duke to achieve the same result. And it is the same with the factory—the one that began well would not require that amount of subsequent effort to maintain efficiency as would the factory established in a hurry, without those precautionary measures which must, at one time or another, be adopted.

The succeeding chapters deal with factory planning in detail, with the product as the basis, and the scheme presented will lend itself to adjustment to cater for the needs of any specific factory in which manufacture is handled upon more or less repetition lines. It is, of course, obvious that the higher the degree of standardization the more easy is it to plan, but it by no means follows that planning is limited to repetition manufacture. No matter how special or varied may be manufacture, it is always possible to "plan," though not in the strictly orthodox and narrow sense exemplified by the planning department with restricted functions. This, however, forms the subject of the concluding part of this book, and may be left until later for amplification.

CHAPTER II

SHOP LAY-OUT FOR A STANDARDIZED PRODUCT

(1) *Planning the Manufacturing Departments*

IN planning a factory lay-out the composition of the product to be manufactured, the market to be catered for, and the production policy of the firm are the main factors to be considered. These together determine the nature of the processes or operations to be employed, the area of the several departments and their position relative to each other. They fix the type of both the labour force and the plant. The composition of the product is the fundamental factor, of course, but whether the product is to be a quality grade for a limited market or produced cheaply for large scale distribution; and whether the factory is to manufacture to customer's order or for stock, are also important issues.

Continuous Production. The large factory plant engaged on the continuous production of identical products, popular motor cars for example, seldom fails to excite in the casual visitor feelings of admiration and respect for the brains which achieve such magnificent synchronization of effort. Actually continuous production is the easiest type of factory layout to plan since, with a standard product and a definite output to be achieved per unit of time, the necessary synchronization of effort lends itself to reasonably accurate calculation. Work can be arranged to proceed in definite progression according to the sequence of operations or processes which the product requires. By suitable balancing of plant and machine capacities specific time elements can be marked against specific output elements. The interdependence of the individual units in this continuous progression arrangement reveals instantly weaknesses due to inadequate performance of either plant or labour, so that reasonable efficiency is assured ultimately.

Factory lay-out for continuous processes is influenced considerably by the nature of the product and its raw materials. Three plans for progressive sequence are possible. The simplest plan is that where the raw material passes through several operations or processes in continuous flow until the final product is completed. Thus, in the

manufacture of coil springs, the raw material, which in this case is
steel wire, first passes to the coiling machines, thence to the temper-
ing section, and so on until the finished springs are received into the
Finished Stores as illustrated in Fig. 1.

Several of such simple sequences may exist in one factory if
different products are continuously produced. For example, formed
wires and spring steel rings are suitable secondary products for the
coil spring factory already mentioned, and if continuous production

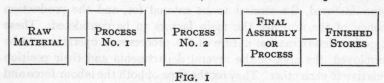

FIG. 1

of these could be arranged for, their parallel simple sequence lay-out
would be the obvious method to adopt.

Another sequence plan is that where the raw material is of a
complex nature and the intermediate processes consist of its
dissection and treatment until several distinct products are manufactured. Oil refining is a ready example. The diagram of Fig. 2
illustrates the idea.

The remaining sequence plan is that where several different raw
materials are employed to produce component parts, from which a
final product is assembled. In this case, which is the most common in
engineering factories employing continuous production methods, the
arrangement employs several simple sequence plans as feeder
elements in the main plan. Popular wireless sets, motor cars, sew-
ing machines, etc., are produced according to this plan, which is
diagrammatically illustrated in Fig. 3.

Job Production. Considering now the opposite extreme to continuous production we have that type where each individual product
is treated as a separate production problem. Steam boilers, bridges,
heavy machine tools and all contract types of product come
under the heading of job production. The product is considered as
non-recurring in exact detail.

Generally the products of factories concerned with job production
methods are of a specialist kind, and this permits of a reasonable
factory lay-out with some semblance of progressive sequence in the
arrangement of the various workshops or departments. A shipyard

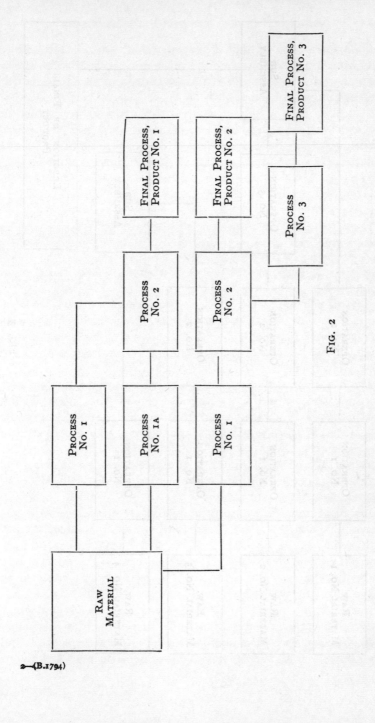

Fig. 2

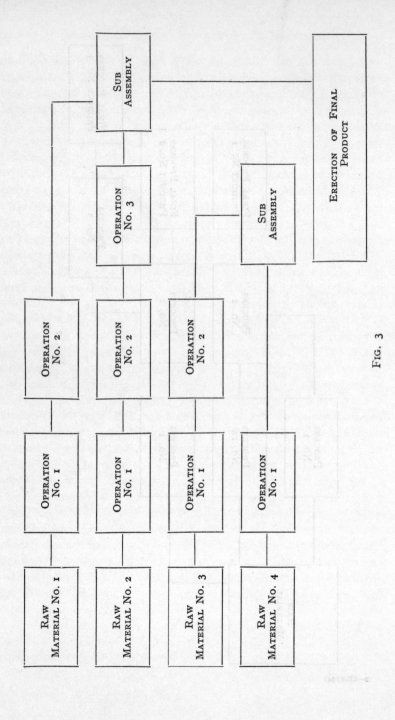

Fig. 3

well illustrates this point, for while every ship produced may be new to the yard in every sense, yet the similarity of all ships permits of a logical grouping of the departments and plant. Machines will be general purpose, however; there can be no thought of setting up machines to suit one product; each machine, even in the case of special purpose machines where these are employed, must be capable of accommodating the variety of work that the differing products will demand.

Batch Production. The most common case in the engineering industry is that where a flexible plant is employed to produce a range of similar products in economic batches. In this case the plant is set up to produce a reasonable quantity of a certain product and then adapted to produce a reasonable quantity of another product of a similar nature. Thereafter, a third product may be engaged upon or the plant may be re-adapted to suit the first product for a repeat batch.

As the various products are similar in nature some of the components will be produced in progressive sequence arrangement of plant, but the greater number of machines will be grouped according to type. It is finding the best compromise between type grouping and sequence grouping that constitutes the organizer's problem in a factory employing batch production methods, and this problem we shall now consider. The materials used, and the processes necessary to evolve these into the completed unit, form the basis for planning, and we may therefore analyse our product in order to see what must be catered for.

We are manufacturing a product of mechanical propensities, the majority of its component parts being of metal in some form, which at once associates our factory with the engineering industry, although certain parts of the product are made from materials other than metal, such as wood, etc. As, however, we are primarily concerned with engineering, it may be said it is this which forms the characteristic of our factory, other matters being more or less supplementary, according to their importance from a manufacturing standpoint.

The composition of our product then may be as follows—

(1) Frame and other heavy parts	. Cast iron
(2) Gears and pinions . .	. Steel drop stampings
(3) Shafting, etc. . . .	. Bright steel bar
(4) Certain small details . .	. Die castings

(5) Screws, lubricators, small parts, etc. Steel or brass (automatic or capstan)
(6) Flat brass plates   .   .   .   Cast or rolled—machine finish
(7) Name and instruction plates   .   Cast or engraved letters, etc.
(8) Trays, covers, etc.   .   .   .   Sheet metal—iron, or nickel silver
(9) Handle   .   .   .   .   .   Turned wood
(10) Case .   .   .   .   .   .   Wood
(11) Bushes, rods, etc.   .   .   .   Fibre or vulcanized rubber
(12) Accessories   .   .   .   .   Spanners, screwdrivers, oil cans, etc.
(13) Finish of unit (main)   .   .   .   Enamel
(14) Finish of fittings   .   .   .   Nickel plate

In planning our factory lay-out, this schedule must act as a guide for the establishment of the manufacturing departments, although in some cases the parts will be purchased from outside sources in a finished state, so that provision for actual manufacturing inside the factory will not be necessary; while in other cases partially manufactured parts will be purchased, this of course reducing the extent of manufacturing procedure in the factory. Processes such as rubber vulcanizing, etc., are handled in the factory only when the firm specializes in this direction and the product is greatly in demand, and in the average engineering factory, therefore, the handling associated with vulcanized rubber or similar products is restricted to machining (in some instances) and assembling.

Taking the constituent parts of the product, as set forth in the schedule, it is for the management (or the planner) to determine to what extent the processes associated with these parts shall be handled inside the factory, and when this has been done, the establishment of departments to carry out the processes can be proceeded with. It has to be borne in mind that the processes involved are very diverse, and that the handling of some will bring into the factory a few of the more remote (from the standpoint of the product) branches of engineering. Let us then deal with the schedule in the sequence given, and see what decision will follow an investigation into the facts of the case.

(1) It is at once apparent that at least three branches of engineering are interested in the structural part of the product (apart from assembling or fitting, which will be dealt with later), for iron castings are produced in a foundry off patterns which must be made in accordance with the design, and most of these castings must be subjected to machining processes before they can be used for assembling. The point to be considered then is how far shall the factory interest itself in the processes involved.

Patterns. The design of the part being in existence, the making

of the pattern is the first consideration. Will it be a paying proposition to establish a pattern-making department, or will it be
more economical to entrust the work to an outside firm of pattern
specialists? The volume of work will determine to a great extent
the method of procedure, which will in turn enable the management
to come to a decision in regard to the actual manufacture.

As the structural parts of the product are to be in iron castings,
it may be assumed that the work in connection with pattern-
making will be fairly extensive, which means that a large number
of patterns will be required. This being the case, it seems fairly
certain that the establishment of a pattern-making department
will be favoured, but before definitely committing ourselves it will
be well to consider the other factors—those associated with the
peculiarities of the product and those involved in the actual making
of the patterns.

In the first place, is the product to be manufactured in accordance
with a standardized design, upon repetition lines, or is the factory
interested in various manufactures, each of a more or less special
character, involving the continual making of new patterns, off which
comparatively few castings are required? If the latter be the case,
wood-working patterns will in all probability be favoured, and,
work being continuous and in sufficient volume to justify its
existence, the establishment of a pattern-making department will
be decided upon.

But manufacture may be upon repetition lines, which means that
the design of each part can be standardized. There may be twenty
or more parts associated with the product which must undergo a
casting process, some of these parts being of fairly large dimensions,
while the others are considerably smaller. It is taken for granted
that die-casting any of these smaller parts cannot be entertained,
as metal of a greater tensile strength than that at present associated
with die-casting is necessary, and so we must consider the method
to adopt in connection with the making of patterns.

The question of size must early enter into our calculations, for in
speaking of large and small parts the term is used in a relative
sense. The manufacturer of one product would call a 2-ton bed
plate a large part, and a pulley weighing, perhaps, half a hundredweight a small part, whilst the manufacturer of another product
would consider a half hundredweight casting a really large part.

The size of the piece in relation to the completed product (or in relation to the other pieces associated with it) determines the definition of "large" or "small," and so, to discuss the matter further, we must have a hypothetical product upon which to base our arguments.

We will assume then that our large castings range in weight from half a hundredweight to one hundredweight, while the small castings range from half a pound to half a dozen pounds in weight. So far as the large castings are concerned, one of each is associated with each unit, but for the same unit it may be that in some instances two (and perhaps four) of one design of casting are required.

We have already stated that the product is to be manufactured upon repetition lines, which means that a large number of castings off each pattern will be required, and that the supply must be continuous. In order to determine what is meant by a large number, we must again refer to our hypothetical product, and decide how many completed units we are to produce each month.

It may be that the factory is to be provisionally planned to produce fifty per month, or, if manufacture is a more simple proposition, 200 units per month, either being considered a "large number," according to the circumstances and what is involved in manufacture. To simplify our arguments, we may take the latter figure as our basis, and we at once come to the conclusion that during one year we shall require 2,400 of each of the large castings, a like number of most of the small castings, whilst in connection with the latter we shall, in some instances, require 4,800 or maybe 9,600 castings.

Before we can decide upon our method of pattern-making, however, we must decide whether the castings shall be made in the factory, or whether they shall be purchased from outside sources. It may be that we are going "all out" for economical manufacture, in which case our foundry (should we decide to establish one) must be equipped on modern lines, which will call for improved methods of pattern-making, or, if we decide against a foundry, our orders will be placed with outside up-to-date foundries, in which case the remark made above concerning improved methods of pattern-making still holds good.

If we decide to commence iron-founding upon a less ambitious scale, however, we must arrange our method of pattern-making accordingly. It is of no use insisting upon the provision of plate patterns for machine moulding if there are no machines in the foundry capable of handling them, whilst, conversely, nothing is gained in equipping the foundry with up-to-date appliances unless these are adequately catered for by the pattern-making department. It is only after the fullest consideration has been given to the whole of the factors involved that the method of pattern-making can be determined.

It may be that, although we are desirous of producing castings by means of up-to-date methods, our resources at the moment will not permit whole-hearted measures to be adopted at the initial stage. Although we are planning our factory to produce 200 completed units each month, this is regarded as a conservative estimate, and not as anything approaching the maximum, our policy being one of gradual development. This being the case, our initial movement is of a somewhat modest character, although it must be strong enough to act as a foundation to our aspirations of the future. We are, therefore, careful to ensure that, whatever method we adopt, that method can be merged, at a future date, with something more ambitious, and this without necessitating anything savouring of drastic reconstruction, and it is with this point well to the fore that we devise our method of making patterns.

We decide, in the first instance, that our master patterns shall be made of wood, and that from these a number of iron working patterns of the larger sizes shall be made for floor moulding. The number of working patterns to each design will be governed by the work involved, bearing in mind the fact that the foundry must produce at least 200 castings each month, and it may be found that, whereas in one case one or two patterns will be sufficient for the purpose, in another at least half a dozen patterns will be required. So far as the smaller patterns are concerned, it is probable that we have moulding machines which will accommodate some of these, whilst the others must be associated with hand moulding.

It will be observed that wood is associated only with the master patterns. This may give rise to the impression that when these have been completed the work of the wood-pattern shop will be ended, and that, in these circumstances, it would be more economical to have all master patterns made outside, thus obviating the necessity for installing wood-working equipment. Were it true that the functions of the wood-working department would cease with the completion of the master patterns, the course suggested above would indeed be the most obvious one to pursue, but we have to take into consideration the fact that we are a progressive concern, and that improvements and developments are for ever taking place. As is well known, much is learned by experience, and when our patterns have been in commission for a time new ideas tending toward more economical production will present themselves, and in exploiting these the services of the pattern-maker will be necessary. Any alternative to an existing pattern must affect the wood master pattern before it can be applied to the working pattern, whilst the introduction of more up-to-date appliances in the foundry will call for further effort from the pattern shop, by way of patterns for machine moulding, etc. There need be no fear that the pattern shop in the factory with progressive tendencies will suffer a total eclipse, for there is always work to be done, even though the department is directly concerned with only the "master pattern."

We have dealt so far only with the wood-working side of the pattern-making, but we must now consider the handling of the metal-working patterns. It may be that these can be directly associated with the wood-working side, but in very many cases the wisdom of this is open to question. Whilst it is true enough that the same principle operates in both cases, it must be remarked that the practice is quite different, for nothing can reconcile the practice of wood-working with the practice of metal-working.

If the volume of business is large enough to justify the installation of a metal-working plant wholly and solely for the production of patterns, then this step must be considered, but even so it may prove an uneconomical undertaking. The opinion of the writer, after many years' experience, is that metal pattern-making can be associated with the tool room far more economically than as a separate proposition.

It is taken for granted that the establishment of a tool department is contemplated, for economical production is impossible without it, and as working patterns are to all intents and purposes tools, necessitating the same care and attention as is always bestowed upon tools associated with the engineering industry, it follows that in the case of metal patterns, the services of the skilled tool-maker will yield the results desired. It may be contended that the purpose for which the pattern is intended is quite apart from the function of the tool, and that, no matter how well the tool-maker may interpret the requirements of the latter, he is not so familiar with the functions of the pattern.

The answer to this is that the determining factor is the master pattern, which is built by the man who has a thorough knowledge of foundry requirements, and that the finishing of a metal-working pattern is a matter of dimensions, which are calculated and set out by a qualified man (viz. the pattern-maker). Also, it is not suggested that metal pattern-making be distributed indiscriminately throughout the tool room, but that, just as tool work is highly specialized—there being press-tool makers, jig and gauge makers, etc.—so also could there be the specialized pattern-maker.

The advantages of such a combination are obvious, for as the equipment ordinarily associated with the tool room can be used in connection with metal patterns, the expense of equipping a department solely for such patterns is obviated, whilst a big saving in floor space is effected. It may also be remarked that, in the event of work in connection with patterns having to be done in the general machining department (and this is by no means infrequent), it is handled far more expeditiously when the instruction emanates from the tool room, on account of its closer association. Having thus planned our procedure in regard to patterns, we may now consider castings.

Castings. It is obvious that we must either have a foundry for the production of these, or purchase them from outside sources, and if we decide upon the latter course, our planning (apart from the supply of patterns) is with a view to creating an efficient purchasing organization. Our decision to purchase castings from outside sources is governed by one of two factors, viz. insufficient ground space to allow for the erection of a foundry (in which case there is no alternative) or our calculations lead us to the conclusion that the ground space could be put to a better use, as the outside purchase is the more economical proposition.

It is obvious that if the volume of work associated with iron-founding is restricted to a few tons of castings each week, it will not be a paying proposition to equip a foundry, unless it is intended to augment the output by catering for the needs of other engineers.

This has been done very largely in the past, and is even now to be commended in many instances; but before embarking upon such an enterprise, the matter needs the utmost circumspection, for unless the manufacturer has a profound knowledge of foundry work the venture may prove exceedingly embarrassing. Too many engineers have committed themselves deeply in this respect, either by accepting contracts for which their qualifications and equipment were quite inadequate, or by reason of the contracts accepted having an adverse effect upon the supply of castings for their own needs. In the matter of founding (as in all other matters) it is well to allow specialization to rule, and the experience of the writer is that the specialized iron-founder triumphs over the semi-amateurish attempts at founding made by the engineer intent upon augmenting the output from his foundry.

It does not follow from these remarks that the engineer cannot be a successful founder, so far as his own requirements are concerned, for more often than not he is able to achieve far better results in this respect than is the outside specialist. These remarks are penned at this juncture to draw attention to the unwisdom of equipping a foundry ostensibly for one's own requirements, when those requirements, unless augmented by the requirements of other people, are not sufficient to make that foundry a paying proposition. In such circumstances it would be far better to rule the foundry out of the factory planning, and purchase casting supplies from outside sources.

But even though we have a sufficiency of casting work to justify the equipping of a foundry, we may still decide that it will be more economical to purchase outside. We may argue that, although our requirement of castings is forty to fifty tons per week, the expense of the upkeep of the foundry would not enable us to produce castings as cheaply as they could be purchased outside, where the founder is producing two hundred tons or more each week. This view may be quite sound if our pattern designs are fairly simple— if our methods of pattern-making are up to date, and if the casting is made from a standard mixture—but if such is not the case, then the matter assumes a different complexion.

It should be our aim to ensure simplicity of design—that is, from a working standpoint, though this does not mean that the design of our product need be of a hackneyed character, for individuality in

this respect is a most important selling point, and must not in any
circumstances be surrendered. There is no need to assume, however, that originality need be elaborate, and if careful attention is
given to the exigencies of manufacture, it is quite possible to infuse
plenty of individuality into the design, without materially enhancing
working costs. In very many cases it is the foibles of the draughtsman rather than the demands of the commercial interests that
cause embarrassment in manufacture, and nowhere is this so much
in evidence as in connection with foundry work.

It may be that the draughtsman, although a capable engineer, is
nevertheless unable to appreciate the peculiarities of foundry work.
He visualizes the finished product from the standpoint of the
engineer, and to attain that which he visualizes he views all constituent parts in the same light. It may be that in the broad sense
he is working upon the right lines, but when getting down to detail
he is apt to allow personal bias to influence his decisions. It is not
so much the actual design as the methods he considers necessary
to produce it, which open a gulf between theory and practice, and
often but the slightest modification is necessary to transform a
difficult and expensive process into one more advantageous from the
standpoint of production. Let it, then, be admitted that co-ordination between foundry foreman, patternmaker, and draughtsman is
the common-sense way of designing an intricate casting, and time
will be saved and a satisfactory casting produced.

Assuming the design to be quite amenable to economical production, in the sense that our patterns can be handled in the general
foundry catering for the needs of numerous customers, we may
decide to obtain our casting supplies through this channel. We
may take it that our purchasing organization will be able to get
into touch with prominent outside founders, so that we can depend
on supplies at a competitive figure. If our product is of a highly
finished character, the finish of the castings must be of a corre-
spondingly high standard, whilst if intricate machining operations
are necessary, these must obviously affect the quality of the material
provided.

Purchasing castings from outside sources requires judgment and
discrimination, otherwise the result will not be satisfactory. For
high class work the low grade casting invariably means enhanced
machining costs, apart from a deleterious effect upon the completed

product, whilst a superfine casting for a more or less "rough and ready" product is obviously extravagant. The type of casting required determines the source of supply, for specialization in foundry work lies in the direction of (a) castings to be subjected to precision machining, and (b) castings required for general purposes, upon which there is little or no machining.

Inquiries for castings falling within the latter category may be addressed to almost any small foundry, but more discrimination must be shown when soliciting quotations for castings of a higher grade. It may be necessary to obtain samples from various foundries before coming to a decision, and then a contract may be placed with a specific foundry for a definite weekly supply. Whilst this is favoured by many firms (and the practice certainly has much to commend it), other firms prefer to deal with more than one foundry, with a view to (a) ensuring supplies at a competitive price, and (b) guarding against a stoppage of supplies owing to the defection of one foundry. If the latter course be favoured, it is necessary to have a larger supply of patterns, and this point must receive consideration when planning the pattern-shop procedure.

But if we have a foundry of our own, it is expected that the pattern-shop organization will be closely allied to it, and this being the case, little need be added to the remarks already appearing under the heading "Patterns." The point to be emphasized is that the foundry must produce the output demanded, which means that the lay-out and equipment must be such as will ensure a weekly output of every type of casting associated with the product. The foundry may be quite capable of producing fifty tons of castings each week (the amount aimed at) and still prevent the factory turning out the number of units required, the reason being that while certain types of castings are produced in excess, other types fall short of the requirement. The facilities provided must ensure that the output of fifty tons per week must comprise the whole of the castings required, and it is this which must engage our attention when planning the lay-out not only of the foundry but of the pattern department also.

Machining. It may be taken for granted that practically the whole of the castings associated with our product must undergo machining processes to a greater or a less degree, and as this remark applies also to probably 95 per cent of the other component parts, the establishment of a machining department must follow as a matter of course. At the present time this department occupies the highest position in practically every engineering factory, and it is here that the greatest scope is accorded economical production.

The aim of the machining department is to set the pace for the entire factory. It governs, as a matter of course, the output from the assembling department, and it must extend the capabilities of the feeder departments. In this latter connection it may be observed that, no matter how high may be the output from, say, the foundry, this can be assimilated by the machining department, and with a little to spare. This does not mean that the foundry (no matter what effort is put forward) can never produce sufficient to keep the machining department fully occupied (this, of course, with the materials received from other sources), for such an assertion would be at variance with fact and common sense. The output from the foundry at one point will probably cause the machining department to devise more expeditious methods of handling it, but when these methods are applied, they will usually be found to have speeded up production to such an extent as to necessitate further effort on the part of the foundry to increase its output, in order to provide a sufficiency of material for the increased capacity of the machining department.

The varied character of machining operations calls for careful consideration in regard to the lay-out and equipment of this department. The type of product, and the method of manufacture (by which is meant the general procedure), are obviously the governing factors, and as our hypothetical factory is concerned with but one product, this being manufactured upon repetition lines, it may be taken for granted that all machining operations can be handled in one department.

The equipment must consist of those machine tools which can most expeditiously handle the processes involved, as it is only by this means that the required output can be obtained. The two points to be borne in mind are: (1) That a definite weekly output must be achieved, and that this must be an *effective* output (i.e. complete sets of component parts, which will enable the assemblers to produce a given number of finished units each week), and (2) that there must be sufficient work to keep every machine continuously employed. Our aim must be to keep the stock of finished component parts at the lowest possible figure, and although, so far as small details are concerned, these must be manufactured upon a quantity basis in order to ensure economical production, the stocks of the larger and more expensive parts should not exceed a two weeks' supply.

It is upon these larger parts that the output from the machining department is planned, and even in connection with smaller details where a number of operations are involved, there is nothing to be gained in completing the whole of these because the initial operation had to be handled upon a quantity basis. Take the case of a small wheel, for example. The first operation is blanking, and it is obviously the correct procedure to produce, say, 1,000, at one setting, but 1,000 of these represent twenty weeks' supply. As three or four expensive operations are necessary before the wheels are completed, the sane method is to split the number up into batches comprising 100 or 200 blanks, putting the batches through the remaining processes as and when required. This matter will be illustrated more fully in a later chapter.

One of the most important points in connection with the lay-out of the machining department is the one appertaining to the transit of material, and the reason why this looms largely is on account of the large number of operations involved. It must be remembered that the more the machining processes are split up (and this is the very essence of economical machining) the more movements of material take place, and adequate transit facilities are therefore imperative.

Inspection, too, is another matter which must not be disregarded, and the procedure associated with this should be decided upon contemporarily with the planning of the machining department. Inspection to-day is looked upon as a much more important function than was the case some years ago, and now, in many of the older planned factories, adjustments are being made for the inception of an inspection organization, and not always with the happiest of results. We shall do well, therefore, when considering the lay-out of our machining department, to decide what form our inspection routine will take—whether the work shall be inspected whilst actually in process, or whether all work shall be transported to a central department for inspection after every operation.

Arising out of this is the question of storage accommodation, for in connection with work in progress one of two things must happen, viz. (1) there must be a "work in progress store" for the reception of parts after each operation has been inspected (this when the parts are sent to a central department for examination after each operation), (2) storage facilities for work in progress must be provided in each manufacturing section (this when inspection is conducted in the manufacturing sections, and the parts, after examination, are sent direct to the section responsible for the next operation). This matter must receive attention whilst the planning of the machining department is under review, and whilst we are on the question of storage accommodation in respect to work in progress, we may seize the opportunity to consider briefly the storage accommodation for raw materials and also for finished component parts.

It is obvious that raw materials cannot be received in the machining department direct from outside supplies, for apart from accommodation, there is the question of receiving, checking, and inspecting of materials thus received, as well as the correct allocation of costs against each job. The method that finds almost universal commendation is for all material to be received and held in a recognized store, and for issues to be made to the manufacturing departments of definite quantities of material upon demand, such demand giving prominence to the specific job number for which the material is required. The demand may take the form of a requisition bearing the signature of the foreman of a manufacturing department, or it may be a schedule or specification list compiled to the instructions of the management, but no matter which method is favoured, the fact remains that provision must be made for a material store, either as an adjunct to the general store, or as a separate entity. The question we have to consider is the extent of the accommodation necessary, and we must be guided in this respect by the amount of material it is considered advisable to hold in stock.

We may decide to hold our stocks upon a maximum-minimum basis, in which case the area required can soon be ascertained; or it may be that we issue work orders upon the factory for a definite number of units, orders for materials being placed upon the outside suppliers strictly in accordance with these. If the latter method is favoured, it is possible that the stocks will fluctuate considerably, but we should be able to estimate with a fair degree of accuracy the minimum intake and plan accordingly.

The storage of finished component parts is of more interest to the assembling shop than to the machining department, the only point affecting the latter department being the necessity for the quick removal of all parts upon the completion of the machining operations. In most manufacturing factories, it is not really feasible to deliver completed details from the machining department direct to the assemblers, with a view to eliminating storage at this point, for the diversity of processes associated with machining renders it almost impossible for the machining department to deliver complete sets of work upon which assembling can commence forthwith. It may be observed that, although the estimated output from the assembling departments is, say, fifty units per week, the machining department must (so far as the individual component parts are concerned) work upon much larger quantities in many instances, and the most satisfactory method appears to be the provision of a finished parts store for the accommodation of completely machined details, and subsequent reissue of these (in complete sets) to the assembling shop.

The close association of the tool room with the machinery department is another matter which demands our attention at this stage, and the planning of the two departments must be contemporary. We may decide that the provision of tools and jigs will not necessitate the establishment of a special department, and if this is the case the making (and upkeep) of tools falls within the purview of the machining department, and the planning of this department is influenced thereby. On the other hand, we may decide to place all orders for tools with an outside firm of specialists, but even so repairs, alterations, and improvements must be effected in the factory and provided for accordingly.

But the more popular procedure is to establish a tool room, if only a small one, and as in our hypothetical factory we have already decided upon this (in connection with the production of metal patterns) it is obvious that we shall "go the whole hog," and establish a separate department for tool production, with a view to keeping this distinct from general manufacture. Consequently, we are enabled to plan this department to carry out what is expected of it, knowing what facilities it will provide for the machining department, and what assistance the latter department will be expected to give to the tool room.

(2) It will be observed that, in considering the structural parts of the product as covered by item (1), the planning of the following departments was involved, viz. pattern-making, founding, machining, storage, inspection, and tools, and of these, only the pattern-making and founding departments are exclusively associated with the part of the product reviewed, the functions of the other departments enumerated being associated with the product as a whole. Consequently, in dealing with the remaining items, it will not be necessary to make more than a passing reference to the departments already reviewed, as in the planning of these due regard has been paid to the claims of every part of the product with which they are concerned.

Drop Stampings, Forgings, etc. For example, although the consideration of the cast-iron details associated with the product automatically brings to the front the planning of a machining department, we do not allow this to blind us to the fact that details other than castings will have to undergo machining processes, and that our planning must allow for this. Because, for illustrative purposes, our product has been dissected in the manner shown, it does not follow that a machining department is in the first instance planned to handle the machining of castings, and then extended to cope with the machining of forgings, etc. The idea of dissecting the product is to show the variations of materials and processes involved, with a view to determining to what extent our factory shall undertake detailed manufacture, and to plan the factory accordingly.

We note that drop stampings and forgings are represented by gear wheels and pinions, and, maybe, one or two minor details. The question to be considered in the first instance is whether the factory will undertake manufacture, or whether we shall rely upon the outside supplier. If we decide to handle the work ourselves, it means that we must establish and equip a smithing department; that the planning of our tool room must allow for the making of the necessary tools; and that the machining department must machine the blanks produced by the smithy. On the other hand, we may decide to purchase the blanks from outside sources, in /

which case the only planning involved is in connection with the machining processes; or we may decide to purchase from outside the parts completely machined, this, of course, obviating the necessity for any internal planning, other than inspection and storage.

Bright Steel Bar. This material will undoubtedly be obtained from outside sources, to be machined in the factory, and in all probability quite a number of different parts will be manufactured from this material. The matter which concerns us in this instance is the amount and the nature of the machining involved, and to what extent that machining shall be handled in the factory, as this must obviously determine the number and type of machine tools necessary. As the establishment of a machining department has already been agreed upon, the complete manufacture of small details from steel bar will be undertaken in the factory (except, perhaps, small screws, etc., which will come up for review later), but in the case of steel shafting we may decide to minimize machining by (1) the purchase of highly finished material, or (2) the purchase of material to the exact length required.

For example, we may purchase bright drawn or polished steel instead of mild steel, preferring to pay a little more for our material in order to effect a saving in machining costs; or, instead of purchasing steel to the standard lengths, and parting these off in accordance with our requirements, we may consider it more economical to allow the supplier to do the "parting off," even though a slightly higher first cost is involved. In the latter connection, however, we have to consider whether or not a "parting-off" lathe (or machine saw) can be dispensed with altogether, for if its installation is necessary for certain purposes, it may not be altogether wise to pay more for short lengths of material in one instance, when the "parting off" of longer lengths (purchased at a lower cost) can be handled by a tool already in existence.

Die Castings. The present-day manufacturer must not neglect any opportunity for lowering his working costs, and the design of the product must show that every avenue in this connection has been thoroughly explored. In our schedule, therefore, we find a somewhat modern departure, this relating to the details manufactured by the process of "die-casting," and, when planning the factory, this must receive consideration.

Unless large numbers of details are to be produced upon repetition lines, this process need not be considered, as the high first cost is warranted only by "mass production," the experience of the writer being that, unless at least 4,000 pieces are produced at one setting, the process is not economical from a costing standpoint. In the factory under review, however, the requirement justifies the consideration of this process, and so we may dwell for a few moments upon the effect its inclusion will have upon our planning.

In the first place, the die-casting process practically eliminates machining, and where it is used to any extent the machining department assumes less imposing proportions than in the factory where the ordinary (sand) moulded iron and non-ferrous castings are in evidence. At present, however, the process is (in this country, at all events) confined to the low fusing metals, so that, in connection with our product, its use is restricted to a few of the smaller details.

Even so, the inclusion of this process has a marked effect upon our machine shop planning, for the die-casted details are those which (produced by any other method) would require a number of machining processes to render them fit for the assemblers. Not only is the turning operation eliminated, but in many cases slotting, milling, and drilling operations can likewise be dispensed with, the effect of these being obtained by the formation of the die (or mould).

As before suggested, the process of die-casting is restricted owing to the fact that only low fusing metals can be employed, but it must be borne in mind that many of the details which hitherto have been manufactured from iron castings have been associated with this method simply on the score of cheapness, and not on account of the tensile strength resulting. In many cases it will be found that lower fusing metals can be used without adversely affecting the utility properties of the product, and wherever this is the case the possibilities of die-casting should be thoroughly exploited.

Unless the process is to be employed on such a scale as to warrant the installation of the plant necessary for the purpose, die-castings should be purchased from an outside firm specializing in this direction, as this will be found to be the most economical procedure. It is unwise to install one or two die-casting machines (which will probably be unemployed for a good portion of the year) and to make special provision for the making of dies, etc.; and where but a few items of manufacture are affected (as in the case of the product under review) the best method is to relieve the factory of responsibility, and invite quotations for the supply of die-castings, these quotations to cover the cost of the dies, in addition to the actual product.

Automatic Work. Under this heading appear such details as screws, nuts, lubricators, and other small parts, many thousands of which are required in the course of a year. In the case of small details definitely associated with the product, it may be deemed advisable to produce these in the factory, and automatics or modern capstan lathes must be installed. If the latter machines are favoured for this purpose, it will probably be more economical to purchase supplies of screws and lubricators from outside, especially if these are to a universal standard (e.g. Whitworth threads, etc.), but if, on the other hand, the installation of automatic machines is regarded with favour, it may be the better policy to create an automatic section with a view to handling all small repetition work.

Before coming to a decision, however, many factors must be taken into consideration and careful judgment shown, for an automatic equipment is an expensive item. The following points, based upon actual experience, may be of interest to the reader and give him food for thought when planning his factory lay-out.

In the first place the decision to install automatics is very often the result of the costly and indifferent product of an obsolete type of machine. In his zeal to produce a better class detail, and at the same time to eliminate certain subsequent operations, the production manager is apt to allow his opinion of the efficiency of capstan lathes in general to be influenced by the product of the out-of-date (and probably worn out) machines in his own factory. To achieve what he has in mind, therefore, the medium which finds favour is the automatic, as being the only practical alternative of the method now in existence. In arriving at this conclusion, he quite overlooks the possibilities of the modern capstan, and it is not until the equipment is installed and in operation that he realizes the full extent of his commitment.

The volume of work, and the nature thereof, may fully justify the establishment of an automatic section, but what must be guarded against is the tendency to regard the automatic as the only alternative to an out-of-date capstan, when improved and cheaper workmanship is desired. In many instances the installation of one or two modern capstans will be far more economical than the installation of an automatic, producing better work at a lower cost, and at less than half the initial outlay.

The manufacturer may urge that the capstan requires the services of a fairly skilled operator, whereas a number of automatics (when set) can be handled by one boy, this considerably reducing manufacturing costs. But for this to be really effective a large number of automatics must be installed, and in all probability the volume of work involved will not justify the installation of more than two or three. If an automatic section comprising, say, a dozen machines can be kept fully employed, then the venture will undoubtedly prove a paying proposition, but if the volume of work to be handled will not justify the installation of more than two or three machines, then the possibilities of the capstan lathe should be carefully considered before the necessity for an automatic is regarded as a foregone conclusion.

If the screws, lubricators, etc., associated with the product are in any degree at variance with an accepted standard, it may be advisable to manufacture these in the factory, for various reasons. In the first place, the quantity of these parts required, although considered large by the prospective buyer, is nevertheless small when viewed from the standpoint of the mass production manufacturer, whose factory is equipped for a huge output of a standardized product, which can be absorbed only by a large number of buyers. His machines are turning out the same type of part for weeks (and probably months) together, and it is only by this means that he can curtail manufacturing expenses and sell at a competitive figure. It is because he can cater for the requirements of hundreds of customers (all requiring the same type of product) that he is enabled to manufacture economically, and the acceptance of an order from one customer for a few thousand parts at variance with the standard is apt to dislocate his programme and increase his manufacturing costs, and a higher price must be charged for the commodity.

Apart from the relatively high price, the question of delivery must be considered, for whilst regular weekly supplies of a standardized product can be forwarded to a host of buyers, the buyer of the non-standardized product must of necessity wait until his own order is executed. When the machines are set for the production of standard parts, these must run for a more or less protracted period, and the "special requirement" will be taken in hand just when it can be made to "fit in," which may not be for several weeks from the receipt of the order.

The "finish" of the product may cause dissatisfaction to the buyer, for the manufacturer is apt to consider the "standard finish" quite good enough for even a non-standard product. It may be thought that the placing of the order with a manufacturer of repute will be a sufficient safeguard, but this is true only so far as the obvious fact that the quality of workmanship varies in the different factories. The buyer may get a product which has a really good "standard finish," and yet be dissatisfied because that finish is not in keeping with that of the other parts comprising his product.

It will be seen by the foregoing that there are many risks attending the purchase of small parts at variance with a recognized standard, although it must not be inferred that entire satisfaction cannot be achieved. These are points which, however, merit consideration at an early stage, and if this is done the right procedure will automatically follow.

Cast (or Rolled) Brass Plates. Our schedule shows that these must have a machine finish, but a thorough knowledge of the function is necessary to enable us to determine whether the part shall be of rolled brass, or a brass casting. If the former, we have to decide whether the plates shall be purchased from outside to the dimensions required (with the necessary machining allowance) or whether we shall shear or blank the plates from rolled sheet or strip; whilst, if a casting is decided upon, we have to consider whether this shall be purchased from outside, or made in our own foundry, the latter only entering into the question should we have facilities in the factory for the casting of non-ferrous metals.

Engraving. It may be that there is sufficient work to warrant the establishment of an engraving department, but if the inscription is of a more or less general character it will probably be advisable to forgo this and place the work outside, particularly if the style of name or instruction place conforms to a standard. Should the design, however, be of a specialized character, with an inscription specifically indentified with the product, it will probably be better (if the volume of work permits) to undertake the work in the factory.

Before deciding upon an engraved plate, we shall do well to consider the alternatives, as a cast or a stamped plate, setting out the instructions or particulars, may be more economical. Blank spaces can be left upon a practically standardized plate, in which can be inserted (by means of steel stamps) particulars of a more or less specialized character.

Sheet Metal Trays and Covers. The manufacture of these necessitates the establishment of a metal-workers' (or tinsmiths') department, unless the whole can be produced by means of a pressing or a spinning process, in which case it would probably be more economical to purchase outside. We will assume, however, that a metal-working department is necessary, and, bearing in mind the expense associated with hand manufacture of this description, we shall do well seriously to consider what mechanical aid can be given.

Apart from ensuring that the mechanical equipment of the department is thoroughly up to date, we shall take steps to see that no process shall be put into the department that can be effectively handled in the machine or press shop. It may be that, although the press cannot manufacture a certain part in its entirety, it can effectively handle certain processes, and this means that our tool-room must be well developed in order to produce the tools necessary for these processes.

Wood Handles and Cases. Many engineers are averse from establishing a wood-working department, for obvious reasons, and if the parts required are of fairly simple construction, it may be advisable to get these from outside. On the other hand, it may be that the case is of a specialized design and is a highly finished product, its function being not merely to protect the mechanism from dust or damage, but also to impart a pleasing finish to the unit with a view to extending sales. Very often it is the "finish that does the trick," and a highly polished wood case (or cover), provided this does not considerably increase the cost, will have a marked effect upon the sale of the product.

Bearing this is mind, it may appear to us the better policy to institute a wood-working department, for by this means we shall at least ensure the construction and finish of the case being to our satisfaction. The outside wood-worker may produce more cheaply than we can, but if we are hypercritical in regard to the product (and in the circumstances there is every reason why we should be), it is more than possible that satisfaction will not be achieved, and supplementary expenses, both direct and indirect, will materially increase the comparatively low first cost.

Not only does our decision to handle the wood-working associated with our product involve the establishment of a recognized wood-working department, which must be suitably equipped for the work it must undertake, but it also involves the establishment of a section to deal with the polishing of the case. It may be practicable to place this under the control of the head of the wood-working department, but, unless this individual is a high grade man, the finishing section must be supervized by a practical french polisher.

In regard to the turned wood handle (item 9) it is expected that, as we have a recognized wood-working department, this product can be economically handled in the factory, as the provision of a suitable joining tool will allow the work to be produced quite cheaply by a low-rated boy operator.

Fibre or Vulcanized Rubber Parts. As these are comparatively few in number, it will be found economical to purchase the material from outside, even though certain of the parts must be specially moulded or cut to given dimensions. There are factories in various parts of the country entirely given over to this class of work, and in view of the technical skill involved in the process, it is distinctly unwise for the general manufacturing engineer to have ambitions in this direction. Fibre rods (for bushes, etc.) of various diameters can be purchased from almost any engineer's store, and machined in the factory in accordance with the requirement. If certain special characteristics are required in vulcanized material (relating to the degree of hardness, elasticity, etc.), the aid of a specialist should be solicited, which will result in adequate supplies of suitable material being forthcoming.

Accessories. This term covers tools and other equipment sold in conjunction with the product, and may include spanners, screw-drivers, oil cans, oils, greases, etc. So far as spanners are concerned, these may be produced in the press shop, although, if they are to a standard design, they may be purchased outside more economically. The procedure to be followed will be governed by the design, and this point should really be settled at the earliest possible stage.

The other details mentioned will obviously be purchased from outside, and they have no effect therefore on the planning of the manufacturing departments.

Enamelling. As the structural parts of the unit are to be painted and enamelled, the establishment of a painting department must of necessity follow. A high-class finish being essential (and at an economical cost), this department must be equipped with up-to-date appliances, such as a spraying plant, etc. This department can easily prove to be the most expensive in the factory unless due precautions are taken, and planning in this connection must follow careful consideration.

Nickel-plating. This involves the establishment of another specialized department, or, rather, a series of departments, for whilst the details must be subjected to a grinding process prior to the actual plating they must, when plated, be passed to a polishing department for finishing. It is safe to say that comparatively few engineering works managers have any knowledge of the technicalities associated with this branch of the industry, and the planning should be done in conjunction with the chemist or the expert who will have charge of these departments. As the majority of the smaller details comprising the unit must be subjected to the process of nickel-plating, the output from the associated departments will determine the output from the factory, and having satisfied ourselves that the equipment of the grinding shop is sufficient to cope with the requirement, we must see that the capacity of the plating shop is commensurate, and that the output from the plating shop can be handled expeditiously in the polishing section.

Assembling. Although we have exhausted our schedule, we cannot conclude this section without reference to assembling, this covering what is popularly known as "sub-assembling," as well as the final assembly (or erection) of the unit. The term "sub-assembling" is used when two or more component parts are assembled together to form one part, as in the following manner, viz.: Bearing, Part No. 561; Cap, Part No. 562; Bolts, Part No. 223. These are assembled together to form one complete bearing, which is henceforth known as Part No. O 561.

In the main, work of this description is handled in a recognized assembling department, although there are exceptions to this rule, which are, however, confined to the minor operations. Sometimes the "sub-assembly" merely covers the fitting of a pin to a certain part, after which the part must undergo further machining processes, and in such circumstances as this it is often considered desirable to have the work done on a fitting bench erected in the machining department. The scope of this innovation depends largely on local conditions and the nature of the work involved, for, with parts of a bulky character (even though machining processes must follow the "sub-assembling") it may be advisable for the latter process to be handled by the recognized assembling department.

Generally speaking, however, the assembling department is wholly concerned with the final erection of the unit, and the preliminary sub-assembling directly associated with it. In other words, the assembling process is sub-divided as much as possible, so that comparatively few separate parts are used in the final erection. The unit comprises, say, 100 different component parts, but 10 of these can be assembled together to form one sub-assembly, 5 to form another, 20 to form a third, and 15 to form a fourth. This means that the erector, in handling four separate parts, has absorbed 50 component parts, and handles in the aggregate 54 separate parts instead of 100.

The assembling department must therefore be planned to comprise a sub-assembling and an erecting section, the former section being again sub-divided if the nature of the work handled renders this necessary. This will be considered in detail at a later stage.

(2) *Location of Departments—Sectionizing and Supervision—Location of Sections*

The position of each manufacturing and administrative department is a matter which requires careful consideration, and although it is not always possible (on account of building construction, ground space, etc.) to plan the position of every department scientifically with a view to ensuring an absence of overlapping, it is possible to triumph over disadvantages by the fullest utilization and exploitation of the advantages which exist. The factory may be comprised of a single building, which must be sectionized in order to accommodate the various phases of manufacture, or it may, on the other hand, consist of a number of comparatively small buildings, dotted about over a broad expanse of ground, some of these buildings being in a remote position.

In regard to the factory in which all the departments are to be housed under one roof, the chief disadvantage will probably be the limited floor space, which not only impedes freedom of action by reason of the crowded state of the various departments (thereby impairing efficiency and increasing manufacturing costs), but also prevents the complete isolation of what may be termed (from a general manufacturing standpoint) the obnoxious processes. As illustrative of the latter, the concentration of the tool-fitter is shattered by the vibration caused by the heavy power press in close proximity, and the fumes and smells arising from the metal workers' section cause acute discomfort to the lathe operators in an adjacent machining section. If ground space permits, the erection of an annexe or an outbuilding for the accommodation of these "disturbers of the peace" will achieve more satisfactory results, otherwise those portions of the building which can be the more readily enclosed should be selected; and this, with an efficient ventilating system in the one case, and a "shock absorbing" foundation in the case of the press, will do much to increase the efficiency of the factory as a whole.

Where the factory consists of buildings set at some distance apart, the largest and most easily accessible building should be utilized for the more important phase of manufacture, the more remote buildings being used for the accommodation of processes that are few in number, or for the manufacture of parts which (save for assembling) can be completed in one section. It may be taken for granted that (as an engineering factory is under review) the machining department occupies the premier position, and the allotment of the other buildings is therefore in relation to this. All machining processes are under one roof, which also shelters the tool-room and, if possible, the finished part store. The raw material store, foundry, and press shop (these being feeder departments) are accommodated in buildings in close proximity to the machining department, whilst the assembling department should not be far away, the more remote buildings being allotted to the wood workers, metal workers, etc., seeing that their association with the machinery department is not very pronounced. This is not considered as an ideal factory lay-out, and is submitted only to show how initial disadvantages can be combated by careful planning. It may also be added that, apart from judicious allotment of the various buildings, the whole factory must be linked up by an efficient transit system, by which means the most remote building will be brought within "easy distance," so that its remoteness will not be quite so apparent.

But in planning the position of the various departments, the same principles operate in any factory, these finding expression in the co-ordination of the different factions, with a view to ensuring a maximum of production. In many factories it will be found that the actual producing time is less than half the time required to complete a given part, the major portion of the time being given over to transport, inspection, and stores routine (issues and acceptances). In support of this contention it may be remarked that in one factory output was estimated upon the time allowance for each operation, the idea being that all non-productive time would be covered by the saving effected by the production operators. In other words, it was estimated that the job for which 640 hours was allowed could be through the shops in fourteen weeks, but despite the fact that the operators earned good bonus, the estimate was a long way from being realized.

It is too often the case that "speeding up" is restricted to the actual production processes, and this obviously necessitates a greater volume of "work in progress," much of which is dead expense from the standpoint of the factory output. The manufacturing departments must be fed, and this means placing in the shops a huge volume of "accommodation work," which remains in a more or less unfinished state for quite a long period.

It is obvious that a "speeding up" of routine will have a beneficial effect upon production, and it is better for the administrative side of the organization to be ahead of the manufacturing side, a fact which is not always appreciated. But "speeding up" can only be partially successful if the location of the various departments is wrong, and it is this matter which must now engage our attention.

In the first instance, the factory is dependent on outside sources for raw material supplies, and the location of the receiving department must be in such a position as will permit of direct communication with the road. It does not necessarily follow that this department must be located at the works entrance, for a road may be in evidence which will permit vehicles to be unloaded well inside the factory, but this does not alter the fact that direct communication with the outside road is essential.

But the location of the receiving department is not governed by this factor alone, for there is the question of internal transport to be considered. The department receives, but it does not hold, and so a destination must be found for the material, which would obviously be the raw material store. This store, being a "feeder" department, must not be remote from the departments requiring the material, and yet it should not be far removed from the receiving department. It may be considered desirable (with a view to minimizing the handling of material) to attach the receiving department to the raw material store, and this is to be commended if the location is alike favourable from the standpoint of receiving and issuing.

As the machining department is interested in practically the whole of the output of the foundry and the smithy, these departments should be within easy reach. The smithy, too, should not be far from the raw material store, seeing that it is from here that all supplies are drawn. Theoretically, the same applies to the foundry, but in practice it is usual to hold foundry supplies in a separate store, which would be as near to the foundry as possible, and if this procedure is favoured the location of the raw material store is not of much interest from the standpoint of foundry supplies.

It is in connection with the foundry output (and also that of the smithy) that the location of the raw material store deserves consideration, for in many factories castings and forgings are classified as "raw material," being received as such in the store from the foundry or smithy, and delivered to the machining department from the store. Should it not be convenient, however, to locate the raw material store equally accessible to both the founding and smithing departments, the same procedure could be followed as suggested in regard to supplies, viz. the provision of a separate store for foundry work.

The pattern shop must obviously be within close proximity to the foundry, whilst the tool room must be equally accessible to the machine shop. Assuming, however, that the pattern and tool departments are amalgamated (as suggested earlier) the position of the combined department should be selected with a view to rendering efficient service to both the machining department and the foundry.

Each separate manufacturing department would have its own inspection staff, but the main inspection organization should be more directly associated with the machine shop than with any other department, for obvious reasons. It follows, therefore, that the inspection department proper will be located, if not under the same roof as the machining department, at least in an adjacent building, so that facilities for rapid and continuous inspection may be afforded.

Closely associated with inspection is the finished parts store, and, if possible, the two departments should adjoin so that, after inspection, the parts can be handed direct to the store without further loading and transporting. It may be considered desirable, however, for all sections of the store—receiving, raw material, and finished component parts—to be housed under one roof, and this may make it impossible for the inspection department and the finished parts store to adjoin. Should this be the case, care must be taken to ensure the location of the two departments being in close proximity, the intervening space being reduced as much as possible, and adequate transit appliances installed.

The location of the assembling department must not be remote from the finished part store, whilst it is equally good policy to bring this department within the purview of the main inspection department. Assembling being the consummation of machining, the closest co-operation is essential, and this co-operation is made possible through the medium of inspection.

In conjunction with the assembling department, the position of the packing and dispatch department must be considered, for whilst, on the one hand, the dispatch department must have easy access to the outside road, it must not, on the other hand, be far removed from the assembling department. Both factors are of equal importance, for the question of transit enters into both cases, and equal consideration to both must therefore be given in determining the location of the department.

It may be that the administrative side of the factory organization is controlled by a combined planning and progress department, in which case the location of this department must be as central as possible, bearing in mind its intimate association with the machining and assembling processes. In many factories, however, "planning"

and "progress" are regarded as separate units, and in this case it
is the progress department which needs be the most accessible from
a manufacturing standpoint. An alternative procedure is to establish the head progress office in the main office group, and to institute
a progress section in each of the manufacturing departments (under
the control of the head office). It is not proposed at this juncture,
to make any recommendations regarding the procedure to be
adopted, mention of them being made only to emphasize the
necessity for taking every factor into consideration when planning
the location of the various manufacturing departments.

We have so far planned the location of the various departments
with a view to minimizing transit expenses, taking the machining
department as a centre point, and placing the feeder and administrative departments in convenient positions. Other relationships
have entered as a matter of course, but in every case transit has
been the dominating factor, and thus the location of the raw
material store (amalgamated with the receiving department) is
determined by its accessibility from the outside road for the purpose of receiving, and from the manufacturing departments (founding, smithing, machining, etc.) for the purpose of issuing.

But whilst transit is a factor which cannot be altogether ignored
in connection with the location of any department, there are cases
where other factors predominate, although fortunately (in many of
these cases) the subjugation of transit by a factor of more local
importance need not occasion embarrassment. The metal-workers'
department, for example, should be nearer to the assembling
shop than to the machining department, for although the latter
department may be responsible for certain processes in connection
with the parts to be handled by the metal-workers, these details
will reach the metal-workers' department via the inspecting section
and the finished parts store, both of which departments are located
in a position favourable to the assembling shop. It is true that
the metal-workers must draw the bulk of their supplies from the
raw material store, which is in these circumstances somewhat
remote, but taking into consideration the relative claims upon the
store of the various manufacturing departments, it will usually
be found that in this connection the metal-workers can afford
to allow other departments, such as the machine shop, to take
precedence.

The wood-workers' department, which is usually self-contained in the sense that it is not dependent on other departments for supplies, can also occupy a somewhat isolated position, and the same may be said in regard to the engraving department. The paint shop, on the other hand, is intimately concerned with transit, yet a certain amount of isolation is desirable on account of the peculiarity of the process. It must not be inferred that the locations of the various departments can be standardized on the lines suggested above, for conditions vary in the different factories, but for the average engineering shop the foregoing will be found a very fair guide for location in the broad sense, with adaptations to suit local requirements.

Having determined the location of the various manufacturing departments, we may next consider the question of internal sectionizing, this being determined by the processes involved and in turn determining the supervision necessary. It is obvious that each manufacturing department must be controlled by its own foreman or manager, who is responsible for output, workmanship, and general efficiency, but where the department is sectionized to handle specific processes, each section must be controlled by a chargehand, who is responsible to the foreman of the department for all matters directly concerning his section.

The volume of work, and the sectionizing of the department together determine the nature of supervision, it being remarked that the supervisor may be of the working or non-working type (in the manual sense). It is obvious that a small department, providing employment for, say, half-a-dozen persons, does not necessitate the presence of a supervisor of the latter type, for there is not sufficient work to keep him fully occupied in a directing capacity. The foreman of such a department would therefore be a skilled craftsman who, in addition to controlling the workers of that department, would nevertheless undertake work of a productive character. Sectionizing here would take the form of specialization, so far as the individual worker is concerned, the duties of each worker being allotted in accordance with his capabilities. Departments in this category may include the metal-workers, engravers, and other work of a specialized character. The wood-working department may in some factories also appear in this category, whilst in others the department may (on account of the volume and diversity of the work handled) call for the presence of a full-time supervisor.

The foundry foreman would not be expected to perform manual duties, as his time would be fully occupied in the direction of affairs, whilst, in addition, he would probably require the assistance of chargehands for sectional control. Assuming the foundry to be concerned wholly with the casting of iron, the department would be sectionized to deal with (a) floor-moulding, (b) machine-moulding, and (c) core-making. The importance of these sections will, of course, be governed by the use made of them, for whilst in one factory floor-moulding is regarded as of primary importance, in another machine-moulding is so highly developed as to reduce hand work to a secondary position. Core-making, too, fluctuates in importance, according to the type of product and the number and character of the cores required.

But no matter how large or how small the degree of importance enjoyed by any one of the sections, the extent of each should be clearly defined, and in this supervision plays an important part. Each section should have its own "head," directly responsible to the foundry foreman, even though in some cases the "head" is but a working chargehand. It will be found that this has a beneficial effect on production, for with each "head" concerned wholly and solely with his own section, it follows that he will achieve better results than will the man who, closely associated with one section by virtue of training and experience, is in addition expected to supervise another section handling a process with which he is not so familiar. Thus, according to the volume of work handled, the foundry sections may be controlled by (1) two full-time supervisors and one working chargehand, (2) one full-time supervisor and two working chargehands, (3) three full-time supervisors, or (4) three working chargehands, but whichever procedure is followed, each supervisor (working or otherwise) should be directly responsible to the head foreman for the efficiency of his section, and not subordinate to the head of one of the other sections.

The machining department calls for supervision and direction of the highest type, and even in the comparatively small factory the head of this department enjoys a status at least equal to that of any other departmental official, and superior to most. By far the greater number of "operations" associated with manufacture are handled in this department, and judicious sectionizing, together with specialized supervision, is necessary to ensure efficiency.

Although in the modern factory matters such as production planning, rate fixing, and the progressing of work through the shops are handled by specialists who are outside the control of the department foreman, the responsibilities of the latter are still heavy enough to call for a high display of managerial ability. It is contended by many present-day factory organizers that the department head is nothing but a supervisor, responsible for discipline, as all managerial matters appertaining to the department are controlled by the specialists already referred to, but to this view the writer is unable to subscribe. Modern organization, instead of demanding less from the foreman, actually demands more, for although it takes from him many of the duties he was never able to handle efficiently, it demands in exchange a much higher standard of effective ability to cope with the possibilities created by the organization.

The head of the machining department then, whether known as a foreman, manager, or superintendent, must, in addition to being a practical mechanic, be also a practical manager, able to control and to direct. The assistance he requires depends largely on the volume of work involved, and a glance at Fig. 4 will show the sectionizing of a large machining department, and what supervision is necessary. It will be observed that the head of the department is termed the superintendent, and that he has the assistance of a "head foreman," in addition to a number of "section foremen." The "head foreman" deputizes for the superintendent during the latter's absence, but apart from this his normal position is one of authority, although (as shown in the diagram) he does not come between the section foreman and the head of the department. He is not in charge of any one section, but controls a certain phase of the department organization, which may include the allotment of labour, designing new machine tools, etc.

The section foremen are chosen for their specialized knowledge —the lathe section foreman being a practical turner, and so on. Each foreman is responsible for the output from his section and for the intelligent interpretation of the principles of the organization as it affects his own section. He may have the control of skilled operator—experience which may by virtue of training and many years' association with the work, or he may be in charge of a section where the work is standardised rather than limited by the accuracy sense of the hand and the actual tending of operative devices upon him.

But without special knowledge of the process he will scarcely attribute... the section foreman is... the foreman only one; the foreman must obtain an understanding, for example of the process, and also of practical application, but he does not mean that he must be the smartest worker in the section. From factor, the foreman was responsible for the class of standard times and the practice of one section foreman was to do the... that I should want that the...

the last would be too hard that the office, not as... has essentially, one point, although at the... the man is bound to a certain extent... be that the following entities... as above are you on each section ... and in-prince and in each line... the workman in the short shop a time or so to great that within the office, as it may carry... faster work.

Thus standing the capacities of one section foreman is still to extent the capabilities of his section or round both the time and the operator. It may be that the selected of the machine the operation is in the hands of a recognised planner as a man in whose case the scope of the foreman may be... Even here, however, they are... capabilities developed, he is one... better adapted, to gauge the particular capabilities of a machine than the section foreman, for it is in the machine that manufacture has been applied at equipment that the... that does not...

The adjustment of the latter's... to... to what extent is... dependent on the equipment of the machine, or the machine for, as saying, that the man is in his right place, it is obvious that the greater the facilities offered, the greater... the productivity of the operator. Even if all labour is carried through the medium of a... organised... experiment... there... is still scope for the foreman in the actual place of operation... although the qualifications of the operator satisfy the employment

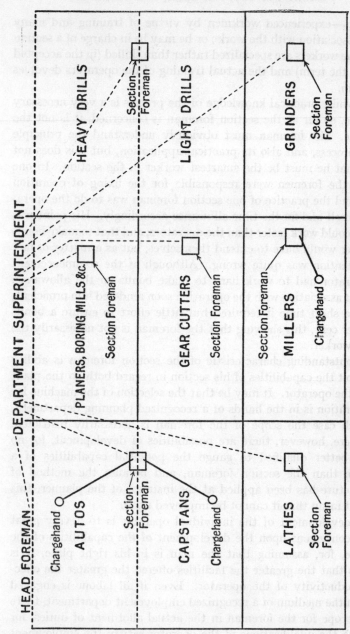

FIG. 4. SECTION SUPERVISION IN A MACHINING DEPARTMENT

DEPARTMENT SUPERINTENDENT

HEAD FOREMAN

HEAVY DRILLS — Section Foreman
LIGHT DRILLS
GRINDERS — Section Foreman

PLANERS, BORING MILLS &c. — Section Foreman
GEAR CUTTERS — Section Foreman
MILLERS — Section Foreman — Chargehand

AUTOS — Section Foreman — Chargehand
CAPSTANS — Chargehand
LATHES — Section Foreman

operators—experienced workmen by virtue of training and many years' association with the work; or he may be in charge of a section where the workers are specialized rather than skilled (in the accepted sense of the term) and the actual training of the operators devolves upon him.

But whilst practical knowledge of the process is a very necessary attribute, so far as the section foreman is concerned, it is not the only one. The foreman must obviously understand the principle of the process, and also its practical application, but this does not mean that he must be the smartest worker in the section. In one factory the foremen were responsible for the fixing of operation times, and the practice of one section foreman was to do the operation himself and fix the time allowance accordingly. His point was that he could work faster than the operators, and that to make bonus the latter would have to extend themselves, but as a matter of fact his contention was quite wrong. Although at the commencement the operator had to work hard to make bonus on the allowance, constant association with the operation soon rendered him proficient, and in a short time it required but little effort to ensure a bonus of 50 per cent, this showing that the foreman is not necessarily the fastest worker.

The outstanding characteristic of the section foreman is ability to exploit the capabilities of his section in regard both to the plant and to the operator. It may be that the selection of the machine for the operation is in the hands of a recognized planning department, in which case the scope of the foreman is necessarily restricted. Even here, however, there are possibilities of development, for no one is better qualified to gauge the potential capabilities of a machine than the section foreman, and because the method of manufacture has been applied at the instance of the planner, this does not mean that it cannot be improved upon.

The development of the individual operator is to a very great extent contingent upon the development of the capabilities of the machine, for, assuming that the man is in his right place, it is obvious that the greater the facilities offered the greater the effective productivity of the operator. Even if all labour is engaged through the medium of a recognized employment department, there is still scope for the foreman in the actual allotment of duties, for although the qualifications of the operator satisfy the employment

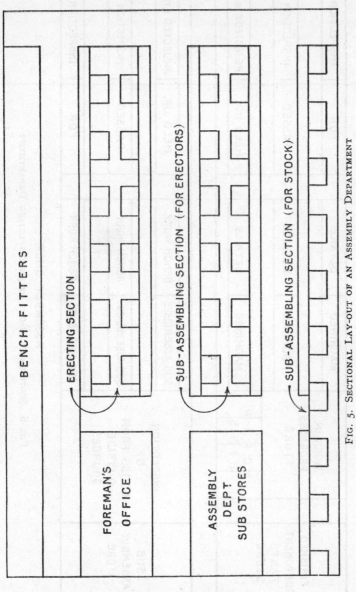

COMMERCIAL STORES

BENCH FITTERS

ERECTING SECTION

SUB-ASSEMBLING SECTION (FOR ERECTORS)

SUB-ASSEMBLING SECTION (FOR STOCK)

FOREMAN'S OFFICE

ASSEMBLY DEPT. SUB STORES

WORKS STORES

Fig. 5. Sectional Lay-out of an Assembly Department

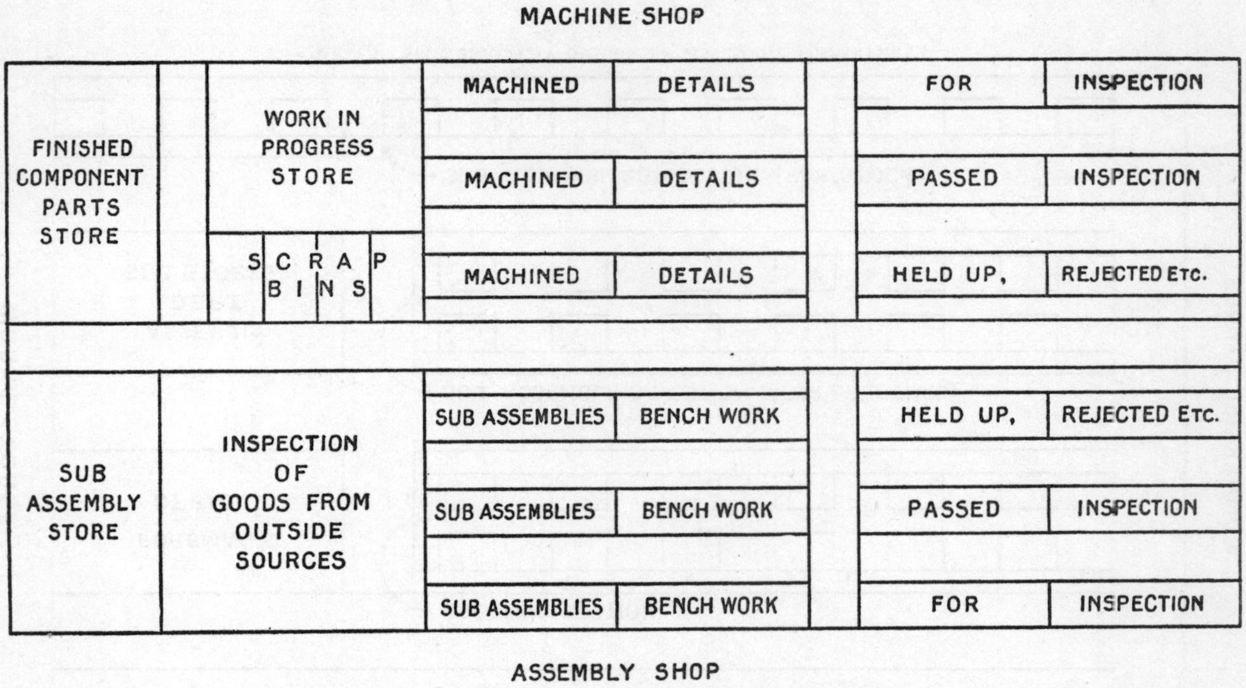

MACHINE SHOP

FINISHED COMPONENT PARTS STORE	WORK IN PROGRESS STORE	MACHINED DETAILS	INSPECTION FOR
	SCRAP BINS	MACHINED DETAILS	PASSED INSPECTION
		MACHINED DETAILS	HELD UP, REJECTED ETC.

SUB ASSEMBLY STORE	INSPECTION OF GOODS FROM OUTSIDE SOURCES	SUB ASSEMBLIES BENCH WORK	HELD UP, REJECTED ETC.
		SUB ASSEMBLIES BENCH WORK	PASSED INSPECTION
		SUB ASSEMBLIES BENCH WORK	INSPECTION FOR

ASSEMBLY SHOP

Fig. 6. Sectional Lay-out of an Inspecting Department

manager, the responsibility is upon the section foreman to get the highest possible return from those qualifications—and this can be done, first, by the correct allotment of duties, and then by enlarging the facilities associated with those duties.

The foreman of the specialized section may, if the volume of work permits, have the assistance of a chargehand or, in the case of automatic or capstan machines, a machine setter. In either case the foreman is responsible for the allotment of the work, the charge-hand's business being to see that the instructions of the foreman are carried out. In the case of the machine setter, who is a qualified mechanic, this individual sets up the machine for the operator and produces the first few pieces, gauging these and ensuring that they are quite correct before allowing the operator to proceed. He is also expected to make a periodical check of the work being produced, and to give advice and instruction to the operator. He is an instructor rather than a supervisor, unless he enjoys the status of a chargehand, in which case he is in authority and his responsibilities are more general.

The sectionizing of the assembling shop is upon practically the same lines, but is usually a more simple proposition. There is the head foreman of the department, who has the assistance of a fore-man at the head of each section. The sections may include: (1) Bench fitting, filing, pinning, riveting, etc., in connection with parts which have to undergo subsequent operations (in the machining department, or elsewhere). This section is in some factories con-trolled by the machine shop foreman; (2) Structural erection of the unit, which comprises the heavy fitting, assembling frame, running-in of gears, etc.; (3) Sub-assemblies of finished component parts, which, when completed, are sent to the store to be reissued subse-sequently in connection with the final erection; (4) Final erection of the unit. A suggested lay-out is covered by Fig. 5.

The precise location of the various sections is governed largely by the construction of the building wherein the department is accommodated, but in this connection there are certain broad principles to be observed. It will be noted that (in the machine department) the sections are formed by the grouping together of similar machines, the capstans forming one section, the milling machines another, and so on, this being generally considered the most efficient method of sectionizing. Unless care is taken,

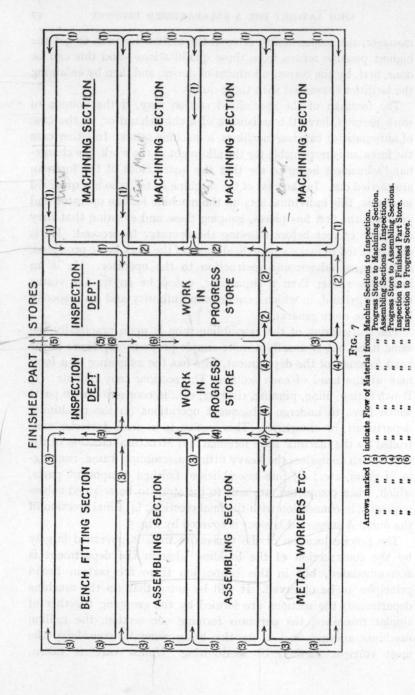

FIG. 7

Arrows marked (1) indicate Flow of Material from Machine Sections to Inspection.
(2)	,,	,,	Progress Store to Machining Section.
(3)	,,	,,	Assembling Sections to Inspection.
(4)	,,	,,	Progress Store to Assembling Sections.
(5)	,,	,,	Inspection to Finished Part Store.
(6)	,,	,,	Inspection to Progress Store.

MACHINING SECTION

MACHINING SECTION

MACHINING SECTION

MACHINING SECTION

INSPECTION DEPT.

WORK IN PROGRESS STORE

INSPECTION DEPT.

WORK IN PROGRESS STORE

FINISHED PART STORES

BENCH FITTING SECTION

ASSEMBLING SECTION

ASSEMBLING SECTION

METAL WORKERS ETC.

however, this method involves a good deal of transport work, as it is impossible (for obvious reasons) to arrange the sections in such a way as to permit the flow of work to be always in one direction. It is possible, however, for the location of the section handling the greater number of first operations to be in a direct line with the raw material store, and so the capstan and lathe sections, handling as they do bar material by way of supplies, should be so near to the store as possible.

It is, of course, probable that other sections (such as the milling and drilling) also handle first operations, but not to such an extent as the capstan section, whilst the raw material used here can be more easily transported. Therefore, the lay-out of the department should allow pride of place, in the matter of receiving supplies from the raw material store, to go to the capstan and lathe sections, the other sections then being located where most convenient.

If all details are sent to the inspecting room for examination after each operation, being then sent to a "work in progress" store for subsequent reissue, the inspecting room and store should be in a central position, so that the time spent in transporting the details is minimized. One method is to have these departments in the centre of the building, with the various manufacturing sections grouped around, as illustrated by Fig. 7.

CHAPTER III

ALLOTMENT OF DUTIES (EXECUTIVE)

WE have already had something to say concerning the duties of the official in connection with a specific phase of manufacture, from which it will be observed that sectional control is recommended, even in the comparatively small factory. The point emphasized is that the efficient control of a department is possible only as a result of the diffusion of responsibility—the activities of the individual being in a concentrated form, his duties being clearly defined, and enjoying a recognized degree of importance. Thus the foreman of the machining department, although controlling a definite phase of manufacture (i.e. machining), recognizes that the phase contains many constituent parts, and that each constituent part is a definite step in manufacture. For example the unit to be produced may be comprised of 100 component parts, of which ninety must be handled in the machining department. Some of these have to undergo more machining operations than others, for whereas in one case one operation will transform the raw material into a finished component part, in another two or even a dozen operations are necessary to effect the same result.

Assuming that to complete a given component part the following machining operations are necessary, viz. turning, milling, slotting, and drilling, it is obvious that when the first operation (e.g. turning) is completed manufacture has advanced a stage. It is obvious, too, that that advance was engineered by someone, and also that human agency is necessary to facilitate the succeeding move, but it is not so obvious that the same human agency at work in the first instance will carry manufacture along through its succeeding stages. The part has been turned, and the actual manual work was done by a man trained as a turner, under the supervision of a foreman (or chargehand), who is also a turner, but the succeeding operation is different from the first, and will necessitate the attentions of another operator, even though the supervision can possibly be handled by the same foreman.

It is recognition of specific phases of manufacture which results in sectionizing (or at least grouping) and by this means we get a turning section, a milling section, and so on. The operators in each section are specialists—that is to say, their skill has been developed to cope with one phase of manufacture. The turner has specialized in turning, although, as a machinist, he can probably handle milling and drilling, but it is in turning that he excels.

In like manner it will be found that the section foreman has specialized in one direction, and this applies also to the foreman who has the sole control of a small machine shop. As a mechanic, he has more than a nodding acquaintance with every operation which constitutes manufacture, but it is in connection with one specific phase that he really excels. And when it is decided that the volume of work is insufficient to maintain more than one foreman in the department, although perforce this department must be responsible for every machining operation, it is the duty of the management to ensure efficiency by providing strength where the foreman is weak. In other words, if the foreman has specialized in turning, and is called upon to supervise not only the turners but the millers and the drillers also, then in these latter sections he must have expert chargehands, to whom he can delegate a certain amount of responsibility; or the standard of labour in these sections must be relatively higher than in the section where the foreman ranks as an expert.

It is probably the case that in most factories the duties of the foreman are pretty clearly defined, in the sense that he is the head of a specific department (or section) and is responsible to the management for the efficient working of that which he controls, but it is in connection with detail that often a good deal of uncertainty exists. In the old days the department foreman was absolute head of the department and directed all its affairs, productive and administrative, but nowadays matters have undergone a complete change. Now his department is planned and operation rates are fixed by specialists, the sequence of production is determined by the progress man, and the standard of workmanship by the inspector. The duties of these officials, or some of them at all events, vary in the different factories—in one the foreman is at the mercy of all and sundry, whilst in another the foreman still reigns supreme, and renders the efforts of others impotent. Neither is good for modern conditions, and it is proposed to devote the remainder of this chapter to an exposition of the author's views on the duties of the official, showing how these duties should be allocated, and how intelligent allocation will make for efficiency. It is the wish of the author to make this exposition of special interest to the small manufacturer, and with this end in view certain duties are grouped together as falling within the purview of one official, this of course applying to the small establishment where the staff personnel must of necessity be restricted. The allocation may be set out as follows.

Sales Manager. No matter how small the factory may be, there must be a department (or section) definitely identified with sales. The real head of this department may, in the small establishment, be the proprietor himself, or, in a somewhat larger concern, the direction may be in the hands of the general manager; but, in either case, there must be an efficient sales organization which can take care of all inquiries received; send out quotations; book orders; issue the necessary instructions to the factory proper; answer correspondence; control shipping or dispatch; deal with accounts; and act generally as the customers' representative. Upon the enterprise and initiative displayed by this organization depends largely the well-being of the concern, and it cannot be wondered at, therefore, that in many cases the principal of a small establishment prefers to handle this part of the business himself.

But an organization such as this cannot, even in a small concern, be handled by a man whose control extends over the whole factory, unless he has the benefit of expert assistance, and it follows therefore that at least one of his subordinates must possess executive ability of no mean order—whose knowledge of routine is no less profound than that of his chief. His ability should be such as to enable him efficiently to control the sales office without the constant supervision of the principal—the superiority of the latter being solely in the influencing of new business.

It will be noted that publicity (or advertising) has been omitted from the duties allotted to the sales manager, the reason being that, whilst in the large concern the matter is in the hands of publicity experts, in the small establishment advertising, if considered necessary, should be put in the hands of outside people to ensure the best results. The principal considers (and no doubt quite rightly) that he is the one man who knows all about his product, but it by no means follows that he is the one man competent to display his knowledge in the form of advertisement. He may have professional skill as a manufacturer, but when he attempts to advertise he reveals himself as an amateur. So instead of "dabbling" in that which he does not understand, he had better stick to his profession and allow experts to do his advertising.

Estimator. The duty of this official is to furnish the sales manager with figures relating to the cost of manufacture, in order that the latter may submit a quotation for new business. In many small factories, and especially in those engaged upon a repetition line of manufacture, the services of the estimator are dispensed with, as with an efficient costing system the necessary figures are always available on demand; but in the factory where the product is but partially standardized, and inquiries are received for various adaptations, the attentions of an expert estimator are necessary. Even here, however, the costing figures form the basis of the estimate, and unless the records are absolutely reliable, the estimate is not likely to be a true indication of what can be done. Where the product is comprised of some hundreds of component parts, and the time allowed for compiling the estimate is but short, it is obvious that, unless reliable figures are available showing the cost of the greater number of those parts, much of the "estimating" may be nothing but guesswork. Useful data can be compiled from the findings of the rate fixer, but the experienced estimator can usually reduce most items to a comparative basis with work already done in the factory. With the standardized product, monthly cost balances show the fluctuations in the cost of manufacture, and with these at his disposal the sales manager can give a speedy and accurate quotation, without the assistance of an estimator.

Chief Draughtsman. The Drawing Office is an important division of an engineering factory. It is there that theory is allied to practical knowledge and initiative so as to conceive, portray and instruct the organization regarding the products which must prove profitable to the firm and satisfactory to the users. Mere academicians cannot be entrusted with this work. The draughtsmen must have both technical and practical training, and they must be well acquainted with the production possibilities of the factory. A successful product must be within the manufacturing capacity of the plant and be satisfactory to the customers in respect of both efficiency and reliability.

The nature of the drawing office organization will vary with the size and nature of the factory. In large factories new designs are constantly required and a large staff of draughtsmen is kept busy. In small factories concerned with one standardized type of apparatus, when once the design of every part comprising that apparatus has been determined, the drawing office work is limited to slight modifications of design as may be deemed necessary from time to time and to the maintenance of all drawings already in existence. In this case probably one draughtsman and a junior will suffice.

The drawing office is responsible for much more than design, and the chief draughtsman must be a man of considerable organizing ability. We can enumerate the responsibilities of the drawing office as follows—

(1) The preparation of preliminary, tentative, experimental, estimating and final designs and data as required;

(2) The preparation of detail drawings for the manufacture of all components, of assembly drawings or instruction drawings for the fittings of units, and of general arrangement drawings for the erection of complete products and for reference;

(3) The compilation of complete Parts Lists for every product;

(4) The maintenance of a system for the organized control of all alterations to products;

(5) The maintenance of a complete records system; and

(6) The control of process copying of Drawings and Parts Lists.

The volume of work to be done will determine the size of the staff, but it should be noted that considerable routine work is involved, and care must be exercised to ensure that this does not encroach on the time of the technical designing staff to such an extent as will curb creative ability. When necessary, clerical workers should be employed for the purely routine functions. But even for the routine work of a drawing office it may be advisable to choose clerks from the workshops. For example, for such work as compiling Parts Lists a suitable shop worker who has had assembling experience could be trained to prove a very useful drawing office clerk.

Item (1) of the above enumeration concerns the senior designing staff. This section may be separate from the main drawing office, or, as is more generally the case, may be the work of the senior draughtsmen in a general drawing office. The work may require involved investigation with stress diagrams and considerable calculation, or it may require rapid rough sketching of ideas for speedy "try out" in the shops.

Item (2) is the most important from the workshop viewpoint. These are the "working drawings." When the product is standardized for repetition manufacture it is advisable that there shall be a separate drawing for every component part. In the case of contract work sometimes several parts are drawn on one sheet. This has the disadvantage that either a multiplicity of large drawings is necessary or that only one part can be produced at a time. Modern practice inclines to separate drawings for each component even for contract jobs. Moreover, with this method the part number and drawing number can be identical and this reduces the amount of clerical work.

Item (3) is an important function for the Parts List is the standard reference for Purchasing, Costing, Planning, Progressing, Storing and Assembling. In it is given all part numbers, related to their appropriate assembly numbers, description of parts and quantities required.

Item (4) is of great importance where repetition work on standardized products is engaged upon. Routine investigation procedure prior to the alteration of such products is necessary to safeguard the capital expenditure on machines and equipment, patterns, dies, jigs, fixtures, tools and gauges. It is necessary, too, to ensure that any change can be worked into the service organization scheme so that correct replacements are supplied. This demands that the point of introduction of the change be definitely established.

Illustration of the working of this "changes section" may be useful. Suppose that it is decided that the cost of one component of a specialized product, which is produced in good numbers in a factory, is excessive, and that the Drawing Office staff has redesigned the part so that it could be more economically produced. The saving which the new part will effect will, of course, be offset to some extent by the cost of new tools, etc., and by the material stock position of the existing part. To make certain that the cost of effecting the change will be justified the Drawing Office sets the "changes section" to work.

First, a series of Change Information Request forms are sent out. One is sent to the Cost Department requesting the cost of the existing part. If all operations on the part are not affected by the

To Cost Dept.

CHANGE INFORMATION REQUEST No............ Part No............

Part Name............ Used on............

Please supply the Cost of the above Part {Complete Finished.
To Operation No............
(*Strike out the inapplicable.*)

Signed............ Date............

Remarks............

Signed............ Date............

	Finished			To Operation No.		
	£	s.	d.	£	s.	d.
Material						
Labour						
Burden						
Total						

Fig. 8

To Progress Dept.

CHANGE INFORMATION REQUEST No........................ Part No........

Part Name....................................... Used on...................

Please supply the following information re the above Part—

Signed......................... Date........

	No. of Parts	£	s.	d.
Material Due on Order . . .				
Rough Stock				
In Process				
Finished				
Total . .				

Remarks ....
....
....

Signed......................... Date........

Fig. 9

To PLANNING DEPT.

CHANGE INFORMATION REQUEST No........................   PART No. ....

PART NAME...........................   USED ON............

Please supply Estimated Cost of the following proposed change ....

....

....

....

....

Interchangeability *is .... is not affected

Note—Give Labour and Material Costs only

Signed........................   Date........

	£	s.	d.
Cost of New or Alterations to Machines, Equipment or Layout	.	.	.
Cost of New or Alterations to Tools, Fixtures, Jigs and Gauges	.	.	.
Total			
Cost of Rework Each	.	.	.
Increase or Decreased Production Cost Each	.	.	.
*Increase Decrease			

Is Pattern* to be Altered or Replaced ?...........
Die

Time Required to Effect Change.........................   Signed........................   Date........

Strike out the inapplicable.

FIG. 10

CHANGE REQUEST

Part No....................
Part Name..................... Used on.....................
Nature of Change.....................
....
....

Reason for Change.....................
Use up Stock* Scrap Stock* Rework Stock*
Is Interchangeability Affected?..................... Is Pattern or Die to be Altered or Replaced?.....................
Due on Order..................... Total Scrap Cost*.....................
Rough Stock..................... Rework Cost Each* " ; " ; " *
In Process..................... " ; " ; " *
Finished..................... " ; " ; " *
Pattern or Die Cost..................... Tool Cost..................... Machines and Equipment Cost.....................
Total Cost of Change.....................
*Saving/Cost Each..................... Approval Signed..................... Date.....................
*Strike out the inapplicable.

FIG. 11

proposed change a "broken down" cost will be requested. A specimen form is shown in Fig. 8. Another information request form is sent to the Progress Department requesting information as to the stock position—see Fig. 9. The Progress Department must contact with the Purchase and Stores Departments for relative information. A third information request form is sent to the Planning Department requesting an estimate of the cost of new machines, equipment or tools required for the change, or of alterations to existing machines, equipment or tools—see Fig. 10. A drawing of the proposed new part (either a rough sketch or blue print) will accompany this request form.

When these three forms have been returned duly completed by the appropriate departments, a final form is made up cystallizing the information supplied and adding such conclusions and deductions as will assist the management to decide whether to proceed with the change. The signature of the Chief Engineer on this form is the authority for the release of the change—see Fig. 11.

Distinctive colours may be employed for the various forms, which are conveniently made up in pads. No doubt the multiplicity of forms will be frowned at by many executives. Reflection will show that by their use much duplication of thought and effort is eliminated and the volume of clerical work is reduced considerably. Whether such forms are employed or not, the information they request must be obtained if a proper understanding of the position is expected. The use of such forms as those described has proved of considerable value in actual practice, in procuring quickly in a standard fashion the information required.

This section is responsible also for the issue of all Suspension, Release and Cancellation Orders. The working of these is considered in a later chapter (page 152).

Item (5). The records system is another important Drawing Office function. In very large firms it is often given separate status, the Chief Records Clerk being removed from the control of the Chief Draughtsmen, in an attempt to separate this purely clerical function. More usually the Chief Draughtsman controls the records department. The work of this department is to receive, store, and control the issue of all finished drawings; to record the release of every part for production; to record the release of every change; to issue part numbers to draughtsmen; to issue blue prints and parts lists as required, and, to control the process copying department.

Item (6). The process copying of drawings will usually consist of suitable blue printing machines; hand operated return types for small amounts, fully automatic continuous types for large volume printing. Parts list copying will consist of straight typing with carbon copies for small requirements and rotary duplicating for large volume requirements. The staff of the department will consist mainly of youths who should be able to assist in the records department when required.

In small factories the Drawing Office will also be responsible for the design of jigs, fixtures, tools and gauges for production. Whenever possible, however, this work should be entrusted to a separate Jig and Tool Drawing Office as the work is highly specialized.

Works Manager. This official is the supreme head of the factory proper, controlling both the production and the administrative sides of the works organization. This is not the view taken by many concerns, and the official known in the factory as the "works manager" is manager only of a certain phase of the production organization. In these circumstances the term is (in the opinion of the author) a misnomer, for if in any factory, i.e. the workshop, there are two officials of equal standing, one of those two cannot logically be termed the "works manager," for neither has authority over the other, and both are equally subservient to a higher authority, who is usually known as the general manager.

There is no quarrel with the decision to call the head of the factory the general manager, and his manufacturing executive the works manager, so long as the whole of the works officials are subservient to the authority of the latter, who in turn is responsible to the general manager for all matters connected with the actual works organization. If, for example, there are two works officials of equal standing, under the control of the general manager, one of whom is concerned with works production and the other with works administration, these could be referred to as the production manager or shop superintendent and the progress manager respectively, but it would be wrong in such circumstances to give to the former the title of works manager when the administrative side of the works organization is outside his control. Yet this frequently happens. There is wisdom in the separation of these two functions, but both the production manager and progress manager should be responsible to the works manager whose responsibility will be to co-ordinate and direct these and other functions.

We are going to assume, therefore, that the works manager is the supreme head of the shops, and that he is directly responsible to the directors or their general manager for everything appertaining to the works. Every works official is subservient to his authority, and all such appointments are made by him or at his instigation.

He will require assistance, of course, but the nature of this assistance is in accordance with the specific circumstance. He himself may decide to undertake the duties of a production manager, or of a works engineer, in which case these posts are not officially recognized. In other words, it is more than likely that the works manager in a small concern will actively interest himself in certain phases of the organization, and it is in connection with those phases from which he is somewhat remote that definite appointments are made. We may, therefore, now deal with the duties allotted to the works officials.

Works Engineer. This official is responsible for the care and maintenance of the factory plant, power, lighting, buildings, etc. He has the control of the millwrights, electricians, bricklayers, joiners, and the like, and is expected to keep all power-driven machinery, machine tools, and plant in a high state of efficiency. He is expected to advise the works manager in the matter of renewals, and in the event of an extension should be able to suggest the type of machine most suited for a specific circumstance. He is not responsible for the actual shop lay-out, as this is a matter for the planning engineer, but he should be able to make valuable suggestions in this connection, whilst he is, of course, responsible for the actual work associated with the lay-out of equipment.

Production Manager. The position held by this official, sometimes termed the shop superintendent, is often regarded as the most important in the factory, for, as the name implies, he is responsible for actual production, and is, as a consequence, the supreme head (under the works manager) of the whole of the manufacturing departments. It is his duty to take the fullest advantage of the facilities afforded by the equipment at his disposal and the administrative side of the organization, and his value to the concern is measured by the percentage of efficiency attained by the works in a productive capacity.

He is concerned with quality, quantity, and costs, and he is judged by the results attained in each instance. His critics are the inspector, the progress man, and the cost clerk, and if he succeeds in satisfying these his proficiency is unquestioned. He must, however, be constantly on the alert, and not hesitate to invoke the aid of the planner or the works engineer in his efforts to maintain or improve efficiency.

Planning Engineer. It may be that, in the small factory, the duties associated with this official are vested in the shop superintendent or production manager, but so important is the function that its separation from actual production should be an early development with the growth of the business. The function includes the devising of the factory lay-out to cope with a given production, the planning of all manufacturing operations and processes, the control of jig and tool design and manufacturing, and the supervision of rate-fixing. The planner determines in the first instance which parts shall be manufactured in the factory and which shall be purchased outside, and he is responsible for the routeing of all manufacturing operations upon the various departments.

Having control of the tool room, he is able to plan the work of this department to meet the requirements of manufacture, and he is also able to facilitate production by providing the jigs and tools specifically designed for the operation.

Rate-fixer. This official is controlled by the planning engineer, and his duty is to fix the rate (or time) for the operation. His activities are largely governed by the system of payment operating in the factory, but, speaking generally, he is expected to calculate a rate (or time) which will prove economical to the firm and advantageous to the operator. The most common systems of payment are based on the Halsey premium bonus system, in which the standard rate is assured the worker, but time saved on the standard time set is shared with the worker. Thus should the standard time set for a certain operation be 12 hours and should a workman actually complete the job in 8 hours his benefits are calculated in this manner—

$$\text{Premium} = \frac{\text{time set} - \text{time taken}}{2}$$
$$= \frac{12 - 8}{2}$$
$$= 2 \text{ hours.}$$

So that, although this workman took only 8 hours to do the job he is paid for 10 hours, and the whole of the difference between the time set and the time taken is still earning time to him.

It is the business of the ratefixer to set the standard times. When possible he will use the average of previous times on similar work. In other cases study will be necessary. For mass production work involved time and motion studies are essential; for more moderate production stop watch observation and deduction will be sufficient.

Progress Manager. The duties of this official vary considerably in the different factories, for whereas in one he is an official of high importance, in another his status is no higher than the ordinary shop clerk or labourer. His duties are, broadly speaking, to facilitate the progress of the various parts through manufacture, by obviating delays of an avoidable character, and by giving such information to the people concerned as to ensure each part being operated upon in the correct sequence. But whilst in one factory he is empowered to direct and control, in another his work is of a routine character; and in order to give a clear indication of his duties in various circumstances, we propose to deal with them under sub-headings, as follows—

(a) *The Progress Manager* occupies a high executive position, and controls the administrative side of the works organization, including progress, stores, purchasing, records, and general clerical work. He is especially adapted for a factory where the manufacturing operations have been planned, but which needs thoroughly re-organizing in order to bring it to a high state of efficiency.

(b) *The Progress Man* is a member of a progress organization of a more or less aggressive type, particularly in a factory engaged upon various manufactures where each order is given a delivery date and this delivery date must be adhered to. He must be capable of estimating deliveries, and have sufficient initiative and power to ensure his demands being met. The best example is the progress section leader in a large factory who has control of one type of apparatus, and is responsible for all the parts involved, from the time the order is received in the factory until the completed unit is dispatched. In the small factory this individual may be the head of the progress department, the duties involved being substantially the same as those already enumerated.

(c) *The Progress* (*or Route*) *Clerk* makes out and issues all work orders and job cards, receives these back when completed, and makes what records are necessary. He does not *make* progress, but *records* it, and it is in this respect that he differs from the progress man. When there is a recognized planning department, the route clerk acts as a link between that department and the manufacturing departments, and, in addition to issuing and receiving job cards, may be responsible for the checking on and off, and for the daily adjustment of a control board or chart.

(d) *The Progress Chaser* is really a junior progress man, although in some factories he takes the place of the latter. His duty is to make a round of the shops with the idea of getting information concerning work in progress, to urge material and parts when required, and to report to his chief when there is any possibility of delay. Although he should be a member of the progress department, and therefore outside the control of the manufacturing department foremen, in some factories chasers are attached to each manufacturing department for the purpose of speeding up supplies for that department and generally assisting the foreman to maintain output.

Department Foreman. We have already dealt with the duties of this official who, as the name implies, is the head of a specific department, such as machining, assembling, tinsmiths, etc.

Section Foreman. This official has charge of a specific section in a department, and is subservient to the authority of the department foreman.

Inspector. The status of this official varies in the different factories, but his duties are substantially the same, viz. to examine material and parts in all stages of manufacture, passing such parts as are to a certain standard, and rejecting those which, on account of defects, errors, or inferior workmanship, fail to reach that standard. In order that the inspector may perform his duties efficiently and expeditiously, he must be free from the control of officials directly interested in manufacture, such as the production manager, department foremen, etc.

He should examine and check all material purchased from outside for manufacturing purposes, and examine each component part after every operation, appending his signature to the operator's order or delivery note when the parts are accepted as O.K., and making out a report when parts are rejected. When parts are definitely scrapped, his report is used as an instruction for replacements. The inspection department should furnish wastage percentage reports regularly to the works manager so that he may be acquainted with the need for remedy at specific points in his organization. The inspection department should not be under the control of the works manager, however; it is axiomatic that inspection should not be responsible to the official who has the responsibility of producing the work to be inspected. Where the inspection function is not large enough to justify an executive directly responsible to the general manager, it should be under the control of the chief engineer or technical manager.

Buyer. The duties of this official are obvious, for he is responsible for all purchases of material, parts, and equipment. He works in accordance with the requirements of the factory, accepting duly authorized requisitions as the basis of his activities. If stocks of material are held upon a maximum-minimum basis, he automatically orders as and when the stock records are drawn to the minimum figure, whilst if manufacture is governed by a "sanction," i.e. an order for a definite number of units issued to the shops at the discretion of the management, he orders the amount of material covered by the specification for that number. In either case he is expected to purchase to the best advantage, taking into consideration the quality necessary to ensure the desired standard of manufacture, the price, and the terms of delivery. He is in most cases allowed a free hand in his selection of suppliers, and by having up-to-date information regarding markets, he is enabled to satisfy the needs of the factory on the most advantageous terms.

In the purchase of equipment, however, he is not allowed so much latitude, as the selection is a matter for the engineering department, whilst the authority of the works manager himself is necessary to enable him to order. The purchase of small tools—drills, taps, files, etc.—to replace wastage is governed by the state of the stocks, such tools usually being held on a maximum-minimum basis.

Purchasing Clerk. This official may be chief assistant to the buyer, or, if the actual purchasing is done by the principal of the firm, as often happens in small factories, the purchasing clerk controls the routine of the buying office. He orders in accordance with instructions from requisitions bearing the signature of a higher authority, keeps the necessary records, speeds up outstanding orders, and passes invoices for payment. His duties are substantially those of a buyer, excepting that he has not the freedom of choice accorded the latter.

Storekeeper. In some factories this title is bestowed on any official connected with the stores, even though the position he occupies is a subordinate one. Sometimes the title is qualified thus: "Works Storekeeper," "Receiving Storekeeper," etc., this implying that the individual has charge of a certain stores section, whilst in another case every store assistant is dubbed a "storekeeper," the supreme head of the stores department being known as the chief (or head) storekeeper. The system prevailing in the factory determines to no little extent the status of the store official and the title he enjoys, as the following will show. In one factory the store is regarded as one department, but is comprised of a number of sections, such as receiving store, material store, component store, etc. The whole is controlled by a head storekeeper, but each section is supervised by a competent official in the same way as are the various sections comprising a manufacturing department. In another factory the construction of the store is substantially the same as the foregoing, but the sections are not so clearly defined, and supervision is confined to one man—the storekeeper—who actively directs the operations of the various store assistants; whilst in a third factory each store is regarded as a separate unit, supervised by officials enjoying an equal status.

Without questioning the right of the individual to the title of "storekeeper," we may give a brief outline of the duties associated with each position forming part of the stores organization as under—

(a) *The Head Storekeeper* controls the whole of the stores department, and is responsible for discipline and for the efficient working of his department, enjoying a status equal to that of the heads of other departments. He controls not only the manual but the clerical side of his organization, and is the official custodian of all factory stocks and stock records.

(b) *The Receiving Storekeeper* receives all material supplies from outside sources, checks, records, arranges for inspection, and is responsible for conveying the material to its correct destination.

(c) *The Material Storekeeper* receives and stocks all raw materials, and issues the same to the manufacturing departments on receipt of a duly authorized document.

(d) *The Progress Storekeeper* receives from the inspector all partially manufactured component parts, accompanied by a specific order form or batch document, and holds these in stock pending receipt of an instruction to issue for the succeeding operation. (This phase of storekeeping is in many factories controlled by the progress organization.)

(e) *The Component (or Finished Part) Storekeeper* receives and stocks all finished component parts (whether made in the factory or purchased from outside) and holds these until authorized to issue to the assemblers.

(f) *The Assembling Storekeeper* holds finished component parts in batches for subsequent issue to the assemblers. These parts may comprise those which have been machined to the specific batch or order number, plus a number of standard parts drawn from the component store.

(g) *The Miscellaneous Storekeeper* issues over the counter such parts as are not covered by any specific manufacturing schedule, and may include waste, lubricants, bolts and nuts, etc.

(h) *The Tool Storekeeper* issues on loan such tools, jigs, etc., as are required in connection with manufacturing operations, also replacements in the form of drills, taps, files, etc. (This phase of storekeeping is in many factories controlled by the tool room or engineering department.)

(i) *The Store Clerk* keeps all records appertaining to the receipt and the issue of store material and parts, such records giving information concerning order numbers, and the quantity of material (or number of parts) in stock at any time. He is also responsible for issuing requisitions for replenishing stock when the minimum figure is reached, such requisitions being placed upon the purchasing department or the works, as circumstances demand.

Warehouseman. This official receives from the factory the finished product, and issues to the dispatch clerk in accordance with instructions received from the sales office. He keeps what records are necessary, and influences manufacture by periodically reporting to the management the state of his stocks (in point of numbers) and the extent of his commitments.

Dispatch Clerk. The duty of this official is to pack and dispatch the goods in accordance with the directions of the sales office. He is expected to know the method of transit best suited to the circumstance; to see that the goods dispatched conform strictly to specification, and to ensure that the goods are in perfect condition.

Time and Wages Clerk. The duties of two individuals are here grouped together, as is customary in small factories. In the first instance the time spent in the factory by each operator is recorded from information derived from the clock card, on which are stamped the times of entering and leaving the factory, and then the time spent on each order by the operator is ascertained by the checking of all completed work orders. The result shows the amount of bonus earned by (and payable to) the operator, and the matter is then dealt with by the wages side of the organization. A wages list is compiled, this showing the name of each operator, his rate per hour, his earnings for the week on a flat rate (i.e. the number of hours worked at a certain rate per hour), and the amount payable to him over and above those earnings consequent upon the number of hours he has saved on production. Then any deductions are shown, and the net amount due is ascertained. This amount having been checked and certified as correct, is placed in an envelope and paid to the operator at the recognized time. The wages list and all completed works orders are at the earliest moment forwarded to the costing department.

Cost Clerk. This official receives from the various sources documents recording cost of material and manufacture, and uses the information for the purpose of compiling costing statistics. His sources of information include all workmen's job tickets and operation cards, requisitions covering the issue of miscellaneous stores, the value of material used, etc. These furnish the prime cost of the job, and when standing charges (rent, light, supervision, etc.) are added, the actual manufacturing cost of the job is ascertained.

The cost clerk should be responsible to the chief accountant. He is not part of the works administration but can and should furnish valuable information to the works manager whose aim is to produce to the required quality standard at the lowest possible price.

CHAPTER IV

PRODUCTION PLANNING

THE degree of efficiency attained by the factory is governed in no uncertain manner by "production planning," and no phase of the modern factory organization has received more attention than this. It is obvious that, to promote real efficiency, the capabilities of the existing equipment must be extended, and no new purchase should receive consideration until this has been done. It is useless for the production manager to protest that he could do better with new equipment, for this is perfectly obvious; but before further expenditure is sanctioned the management must know that the maximum is being obtained from what is existing, and that that maximum is not enough.

It is difficult, indeed, to assert that the peak has been reached, for ingenuity has the knack of giving the lie to the assertion. Under certain conditions the maximum is quickly reached, but then conditions are subject to change, and the change has the effect of increasing the maximum. In the first place the methods of manufacture may be quite elementary, every detail comprising the unit being made in the factory. On these lines the maximum output may equal fifty sets of details per week, but now it is decided to purchase certain details from outside, and with the equipment freed by this procedure it is possible to handle larger quantities of other parts, with the result that the maximum is increased to seventy. Improved methods of manufacture made possible by the provision of up-to-date tools and jigs may further increase the maximum to ninety, and the introduction of a carefully devised bonus system may bring the weekly production figure well over 100.

But now, surely, it is not possible to increase further without new equipment, and the latest figure must of necessity be the peak. It may be so, but it is by no means certain, for action may now be taken in the direction of die-casting or a similar process, devised for reducing machining to a minimum. It is obvious that such action on a fairly large scale will once again increase the capabilities of the manufacturing departments, and it is safe to say that the output of the progressive factory can, in a few years, increase 400 or 500 per cent, and this with comparatively little additional capital outlay.

It may be argued that such an increase is possible only in the factory where the methods in the first instance are so elementary that even a slight attempt at reorganization cannot help but increase output considerably, but if this is the case, then the methods favoured by many so-called up-to-date concerns are extremely elementary. The truth is that no matter what methods prevail in the factory these can be improved upon, and the reason that one concern forges ahead of the others is because the management of that concern realizes the truism, and is continually affecting improvements.

The important bearing that "production planning" has upon a progressive factory output is recognized to-day in almost every works, but in many of the smaller concerns the activities of the management in this direction are limited to what is in reality "operation planning." This, whilst yielding a certain return, is by no means an unqualified success, for it may be likened to the building of a house upon an insecure foundation. The fact is that the reform is undertaken, not by the management as a whole but by that section of the management devoted to purely works matters. An "operation planner," or "process fixer," is introduced into the factory, and his business is to do the best with what is already existing. He has no power to effect reforms in connection with the design or the specification—he can plan the operations for machining a steel shaft from bar material, but he cannot supersede that bar material by a forging.

Production planning, to be really effective, must commence with the design, and if the design has been in existence for some years it must be subjected to a drastic overhaul, and the specification revised to meet the exigencies of the factory equipment. It is usually the case (in the small factory, at all events) that the design is the fancy of the inventor, and the actual means of producing the finished part is rarely considered. On the other hand, the equipment provided in the factory is of a standardized character—so many capstans up to 1 in., so many up to 2 in., so many engine lathes, milling machines, and so on. It is on account of this that there are so many "difficult jobs" in the factory, because there is no machine really suitable for the work, and when, at a later date, "operation planning" is introduced, these "difficult jobs" are the despair of the planner, and excite the ire of the operator.

In an earlier chapter we sought to obviate this by arranging the factory lay-out in accordance with the specification of the product, but it was assumed that the specification had been compiled from a really practical standpoint. If one detail is specified as a casting, a casting will fill the bill better than anything else, taking into proportionate consideration the claims of utility, economy, and practicability.

And the design of that casting? Here again there is likely to be a divergence of opinion, for often needless expense is occasioned in the workshop which could be obviated as a result of a very slight adjustment of the design. It is inevitable that the ideas of the designer and the factory man differ, for the former takes a broad survey and applies theoretical knowledge to the problem, whilst the latter views the problem from the narrower standpoint of practicability.

It is clearly necessary that the two should meet, and the "common ground" is provided by production planning. It is distinctly unwise to allow the designer absolute freedom, for by so doing really economical manufacture is quite out of the question. On the other hand, the views of the shopman must not be accepted without comment, for apart from the fact that he is not qualified to deal with the matter from the standpoint of utility, he is not always competent to "say the last word" in respect to actual manufacture. We have just now asserted that practicability is the narrower viewpoint, in the sense that the views of the shopman are formed by his personal understanding of the immediate environment. He may have had a broad practical experience, but that experience is of men and machines, and his estimate of their capabilities is based largely upon personal observation, which is a by no means infallible guide.

His practical experience enables him to say "this can be done," "this cannot be done," or "this can only be done a certain way"; but another man will advance a different opinion in each instance. From this it will be seen that opinions, even when backed by practical experience, form an insecure foundation for production planning, and the adage old that "two heads are better than one " should be always kept in mind when the fundamentals of factory organization are being considered.

The best combination in this connection is undoubtedly that of the designer and the planner, and assuming that each is proficient in his own line of business, the outcome is sure to be satisfactory. The planner is at all times a severe critic of design, but in the main his arguments are but partially successful, due to the unwritten law that design is sacred, and must not be subjected to any indignity. But when the designer is compelled to submit his conclusions to the judgment of the man responsible for manufacture, and when the planner is empowered to insis on his criticisms and suggestions receiving consideration, there is every possibility of a compromise being effected which will have an important bearing upon efficiency in the workshop.

It may be contended by some that the outcome will be a deadlock; each man obstinately clinging to his beliefs and refusing to give way even in the smallest particular, but this is to be feared only when the proficiency of the opposing parties is open to question. In actual practice it has been found that, the higher the state of proficiency attained by the individual the more open is that individual to conviction, and the more inclined is he to give consideration to the opinions of others. Most industrial troubles are due to the vapouring of those who do not sincerely believe in what they preach (though many affect to do so), whilst mismanagement may be attributed to those who are obstinately determined to carry through their own ideas, although they know that those ideas are not virile enough to support the load they are expected to carry.

If a new product is about to be put into process of manufacture, the co-operation between the designer and the factory planner will enable production planning to commence on a high level, for a clean slate is in evidence, not disfigured by the lines representing the activities of those who have gone before, which lines are often an obstruction bristling with difficulties. But if, on the other hand, the design is old, and the product is regarded as more or less standardized, the lines on the slate are clearly discernible and must be obliterated before progress can be made.

Here the drawing of every component part must be scrutinized, and the necessary modifications made. The part as it exists may be satisfactory from one standpoint, but not from another, and so the problem must be tackled. Many factors must be taken into consideration, and changes must not be effected lightly, for the product is really an assembly of a number of sub-assemblies, and few, indeed, of the parts stand alone, in the sense that no other part is affected by an alteration. It is not even sufficient to consider under one heading the whole of the parts comprising one sub-assembly, for that sub-assembly may engage with another, and changes of a beneficial character here may have untoward effects elsewhere.

One illustration will serve to show how even a trivial alteration will sometimes cause trouble when one factor is overlooked. When the design was being overhauled it was agreed that the amount of metal which comprised one small part (a casting) could be reduced, as there was apparently no need for it. The change was made, but when at length the new part was used for assembling, it was discovered that a stop pin was necessary to enable it to operate. That extra bit of metal on the old part made the provision of a stop pin unnecessary, as it prevented the other end of the detail coming farther than desired, but by reducing the metal by the merest fraction of an inch, the creation of a stop pin was necessary to enable the part to function properly.

Assuming that a perfect understanding exists between the designer and the planner, it should not be difficult for the latter to map out the course of manufacture. He has a fairly comprehensive knowledge of the capabilities of the factory equipment, and knowing the expectations of the management in regard to output, he should be able to plan, first broadly, and then in detail. It has been agreed that the equipment is capable of meeting the demand, subject to the provision of jigs and tools in certain circumstances, and in the broad sense, at all events, there should be no difficulty in ensuring an equitable distribution of work throughout the manufacturing departments.

Some planners stop at this point, and expect the more detailed planning to be arranged by the various department foremen. In other words, the planner decides that a certain detail shall be turned, and fixes a price for this operation. The operation is, however, but broadly defined, and a detailed consideration will elicit the fact that in reality it is made up of quite a number of smaller operations.

It is in this respect that the planner solicits the active co-operation of the department foreman, for the latter is expected to plan to such good purpose that the cost of the operation is considerably under the price allowed. He must dissect the operation and manipulate labour with this end in view, using the lowest grade labour commensurate with the standard of workmanship desired.

It may be said at once that this method is by no means satisfactory for a variety of reasons. In the first place, the operation as a whole may be dissected into, say, three sub-operations, the first of which can be handled by a second grade operator, the second by a third grade operator, whilst the third must engage the attentions of an operator of the highest class. As the price covers the operation as a whole, it means that one operator must be selected for the task, and where one of the sub-operations must be handled by a high grade man, it means that this individual must also handle the other operations involved, which is by no means an economical proposition.

Another point to be considered is that, in the circumstances mentioned, the use of tools and jigs for facilitating production is restricted. It is quite likely that certain tools and jigs are devised, but they are not nearly so effective as when the operation lay-out is carefully drafted by the planning department, and the tool or the jig is made specifically for the job. When the operation is dissected by the foreman, it is often found that the tools provided somehow do not fit in with the scheme of things, and the use of "temporary" tools and fixings, devised and made by the foreman or the operator, is resorted to.

Again, because in one instance the foreman adopts a certain course for the purposes of dissection, it by no means follows that he will adhere to that course when a subsequent batch of similar parts is to be operated upon. His method is to utilize his operators and his equipment to the best advantage "according to the circumstances," and the method deemed the most advantageous to-day may be (in his opinion) quite out of court a month hence, due to "changing circumstances." Uniformity of manufacture cannot be guaranteed under such conditions, and, in the factory where production is upon repetition lines, the operation lay-out down to the smallest detail should be in the hands of a recognized planner.

It will be appreciated that, as the selection of the plant has been made with due regard to the product to be manufactured, and the design of the parts comprising the product is the outcome of careful consideration in relation to the plant, the circumstances are most favourable to economical production, assuming that this happy state of affairs is not allowed to deteriorate by injudicious handling. Even the handling has been taken care of in at least one direction, for the lay-out of the manufacturing departments and the grouping of machines has already been effected, and all that remains is to ensure that the fullest advantage is taken of all this careful planning. And it is now that intelligent operation planning must receive consideration.

It is assumed that a bonus system in some form will prevail. The payment for production work on a flat hourly rate is being discarded even in the smallest of factories, and in its stead is being instituted a method of payment which provides an incentive to the operator. There is no gainsaying the fact that, for repetition work at all events, a bonus system of payment is necessary to ensure economical production, as with it output is increased, manufacturing costs are reduced, workmanship is better, and a better feeling prevails in the factory.

The last two statements may be questioned by some, but the writer's opinion is based upon practical experience in many factories, both large and small. That in some cases work is scamped through the operator going "all-out for bonus," and that the system of payment is directly responsible for a good deal of discontent, is freely admitted, but if the cases are investigated it will be found that it is not the *principle* of the system that is at fault but the method of application. In other words, the trouble is entirely due to unscientific and unfair operation planning.

It is an undeniable fact that, in the competitive shop, a bonus system is essential. Many of those people who claim that the "day rate" system is superior, base their assertion upon the peaceful atmosphere prevailing in the old-established "jog-trotting" concern. Here there is no hustle and no anxiety—the employees are old servants who are happy and contented, and workmanship reaches a very high standard. Incidentally, whilst there is always enough work to keep the shops fully employed, there is not enough for the management to doubt the capacity of the factory to accommodate it without extending, for the price is high and the demand as a consequence is limited.

Such a firm has a virtual monopoly of the type of apparatus it manufactures, and it trades solely upon its reputation. There is no necessity to offer incentives to the workers to produce quicker and cheaper—a good wage is paid for good workmanship, and good profits are made by the firm. But all firms are not in this happy position—they must compete for orders against powerful rivals. They have not a monopoly of the product; a score of firms are manufacturing a similar article, and it is only by the development of an efficient manufacturing procedure that the article is produced at a cost that will permit an adequate market to be found.

This being the case, the advantages of an "incentive" are obvious, but the reward must be there. Some firms adopt operation planning and fix rates, and then, when these have been in operation for a few months, go "all-out" for rate-cutting on the score that the workers are earning too much. Others fix the rates at a figure that will not allow the man to earn over his flat weekly wage, no matter how hard he works, and, as may be expected, he soon ceases to strive after the impossible, contenting himself to do just as much as will enable him to keep his job. Other firms again institute a somewhat complicated system of rate-setting, whereby a certain percentage of the time saved by the operation is put to the credit of the firm, and, the working of this not being thoroughly understood, a good deal of unrest and discontent is speedily apparent.

The small manufacturer will do well to ignore these complicated systems, and adopt a simple and straightforward scheme that gives the operator all that he saves without any deduction. The firm can cover itself in the matter of capital expenditure by way of creating facilities by intelligent operation planning. The contention that the firm is entitled to a certain percentage of the bonus earned by the operator, because of the expense in making the tool which made the operation possible, is justified only when the rate fixed is high enough to permit that percentage to be deducted from the operator's earnings, which means that the firm has to give before it can receive. But if the operation rate is fixed after taking into consideration the claims of the firm relative to the cost of the tool, the matter assumes more simple proportions, for the saving effected speedily absorbs the cost of the tool.

Rate-setting that yields abnormally high results by way of bonus is obviously uneconomical, and it is at once apparent that the person responsible for the rate knew little of the operation, or of the facilities provided. Attempts at rate-cutting are fiercely combated by the operators, who adopt a "go slow" policy in order to keep the bonus amount within reasonable limits. It is not enough for the rate-setter to know all about the theoretical capacity of the machine by means of feed and speed calculations, but he must also know the capabilities of the machine in relation to the specific job, the special facilities provided for that job, and the capabilities of the operator.

This latter is most important, for it is in many cases an unknown quantity. Many progressive firms to-day appreciate this, and are endeavouring to sound the depths of individual capability by means of vocational selection. It is an endeavour to quicken the leanings of the individual, and to develop his potential capabilities in the direction to which they will the most readily respond.

Every person has a "leaning," and could that leaning be detected and fostered, the highest state of efficiency would be the result. Unfortunately, the expressed desire of the individual is not always indicative of the primary talent, for even the most intense interest one evinces in a certain direction will not always produce capability which equals 100 per cent efficiency.

This capability must be sought for, and may be found through the medium of vocational selection. Briefly, it is getting the right man for the job, or, conversely, getting the job right for the man, and unless the capabilities of the operators are known, operation planning can never give the best results.

Another science which is now being exploited for the benefit of economical manufacture is that known as "motion study," and although the small manufacturer may protest that this is too complex to merit his consideration, its elementary principles might prove advantageous to him. These may, for the purposes of convenience, be labelled "facilities," devised with a view to relieving strain and lessening fatigue, and although to some people the word "fatigue" may mean "that tired feeling, born laziness," it will occur to any intelligent factory manager that nothing is gained by making the operators tired as a result of superfluous activity.

No man will make two journeys when one will suffice. No man

will walk 100 yards when his purpose can be served by walking 30, and no man will throw things down just for the pleasure of picking them up again. Yet, in effect, this is what is happening in scores of factories, and the management wonders why manufacture costs so much. It does not seem to be appreciated that, not only is there a senseless waste of time, but the operator tired out by unnecessary actions is unable to give of his best when actually engaged upon production. Let us give a few illustrations—and suggestions.

(1) The operator completes his job and walks to the office for another job card. Returning to his place he finds that he requires a certain tool, so walks to the tool store to get it.

Could not this job card, drawing (if necessary), and the tool be handed out together, or at least during the one journey?

(2) The material store is situated at one end of the factory, remote from the manufacturing departments, a good deal of time being wasted in the transport of material.

Could not the material store be within close proximity to the manufacturing departments, and thus minimize transport time?

(3) Parts are brought by a labourer from the store and packed on the floor near to the operator's machine. As the operator completes his work the parts are again placed on the floor, being afterwards picked up by a labourer for conveyance to the inspection department.

Could not the parts be conveyed in a box to the operator, with another box available for putting in the parts as completed, thus reducing handling to a minimum?

(4) Unnecessary strain is imposed on the operator owing to the fact that benches are too high or too low, and also on account of continuous standing.

Could not the benches be made a convenient height, or adjustable, and could not seats be provided in certain circumstances?

(5) Unnecessary movements are caused by the operator having to reach for the various tools, etc., which are scattered about the bench or upon the floor.

Could not tool holders or receptacles be provided and placed in a handy position?

Many more examples could be quoted and will no doubt occur to the reader, but sufficient has been said to demonstrate the importance of this factor, which must not be disregarded by the manager whose aim is efficiency and economy.

Having considered all preliminary matters, the actual business of operation planning may now be taken in hand, and in this connection the recognized procedure is to take each component part, decide what is necessary to transform the raw material into a finished part, what finished parts shall come together to form a sub-assembly, and the procedure to bring sub-assemblies to form the completed unit.

Referring to the drawing of the component part, we must first observe its origin, then the nature of the metal to be used and the process necessary to render this metal suitable for machining. The origin may be a casting or a forging, the metal iron or brass, and the process moulding and casting, or forging or drop-stamping. On the other hand, the origin may be bar stock, material brass or steel, and as this material is held as standard stock, no preliminary process is necessary to make it suitable for machining.

The preliminary process should be treated separately; that is to say, the operations associated with the foundry or the smithy should be kept apart from the operations associated with machining. The latter should commence with the raw material as regarded from a machining standpoint, whether this raw material is represented by a casting, stamping, or bar steel or brass.

For the purposes of this chapter, we will commence with operation planning at the point where the material is ready for machining, as this will give us the best idea of the procedure to be followed. Each component part is given a number for the purposes of identification, and this number also enables us to file cards and documents for easy reference. The operations have to be planned in correct sequence, and care taken to see that the handling of one operation does not adversely affect the result of a preceding operation.

The first machining operation having been determined, the next business is to decide just how this should be done—if parting-off, is this to be done on a lathe or a power saw?—if centring, is this to be done on a lathe or a drilling machine? Sometimes an operation is necessary simply to enable a jig to be used in connection with another operation, and again, an operation may be displaced from what might be regarded as its correct sequence, for a similar reason.

The machining department is sectionized, which means that all turning operations will be handled in the turning section, all milling operations in the milling section, and so on; but there is often a big variation in the equipment of a section, and in many cases the precise machine must be specified. To assist in this direction, a machine register is compiled, this giving the name and brief particulars of every machine. This register is illustrated by Fig. 12.

REGISTER OF MACHINES

No.	Type	Make	Location	Capacity
1	Auto Screw m/c	Moulton	Shop E	$\frac{1}{4}''$ bar
2	,,	,,	,,	$\frac{5}{16}''$,,
3	,,	,,	,,	$\frac{3}{8}''$,,
4	Bar Capstan	Bardon	,,	$1\frac{1}{4}''$,,
5	Turret	Ward	,,	Up to $1''$ bar
6	,,	—	,,	With adapter for chucking
7	Saw	No. 18	Shop F	Screw slotting up to 2 B.A.
8	,, (Bench)	,, 20	,,	Up to $\frac{1}{4}''$ plate
9	Capstan (Bench)	,, 14	,,	$\frac{5}{16}''$ brass
10	Miller	,, 26	,,	Auto-feed $9'' \times 4'' \times 10''$
11	,,	,, 27	,,	,, ,,
12	Press	,, 31	,,	Power—20 ton
13	Fly Press	B. & H.	,,	Hand
14	Miller	No. 28	,,	Hand-feed $12'' \times 6'' \times 12''$
15	Drill	,, 25	,,	
16	,,	,, 24	,,	
17	,,	,, 23	,,	

FIG. 12

The operators are divided into three grades: Grade 1 comprising the highly skilled workers; Grade 2 specialized workers; and Grade 3 comparatively inexperienced workers, such as young boys and girls. The planner is aware of the grade of labour operating the various machines, and this assists him in the allotment of work to the machine, assuming that the principle previously advocated is put into practice, and the right man for the job is chosen.

OPERATION SHEET

Compiled by............*C. H. J*..............　　　　Date............24/8/............
Checked by.................*F. W.*............　　　　Date............25/8/............
For........*Tube and Arbor Details and Sub-assemblies*........　Type........*Z*.........

Component Part No.	Description	Operation No.	Operation	Machine No.	Grade of Labour	Setting Time	Time Allowed (mins. each)	For Sub-assembly
214	Tube	1	Part off	10	2	¼ hr.	1·0	
		2	Form	15/18	1	1 hr.	2·0	
		3	Drill	80	3	¼ hr.	·857	
								A214
215	Hook	1	Form	21/22	2	1 hr.	1·72	
								A214
A214	S/A 214, 215	1	Rivet	Bench	3		2·5	
		2	File	,,	2		1·3	
								A216
216	Cap	1	Blank	53	3	½ hr.	·33	
		2	Flatten	54	3		·66	
		3	Face and Form	9	1	2 hr.	2·0	
		4	Drill	81/83	3		·5	
								A216
A216	S/A A214, 216	1	Fit Cap	20	1		3·0	
		2	Turn True	84	1		4·0	
		3	Bore	91	1		4·0	
								AA217
217	Arbor	1	Form	30	2	4 hr.	4·0	
		2	Mill	51	1	½ hr.	3·0	
		3	Drill and C/Sk	81/83	3	¼ hr.	1·3	
								A217
218	Rivet	1	Form	21/22	2	1 hr.	1·72	
								A217
A217	S/A 217, 218	1	Rivet	Bench	3		2·5	
		2	File	,,	3		1·3	
								AA217
AA217	S/A A216, A217	1	Assemble	Bench	2		5·0	
		2	Finish	,,	1		2·0	
								Final

FIG. 13

When operation planning is in process, an operation sheet or route card (similar to Fig. 13) is compiled. This records the operation in the correct sequence, the machine number, the grade of labour, the tool number associated with the operation, the time allowance for machine setting (if necessary) and for the operation, the standard quantity upon which the time allowance is based, etc. In regard to the last clause it will be observed that, although the time allowance is calculated per piece, it is obvious that an economical allowance is possible only on quantity production, and that the bigger the quantity handled at one setting (subject to certain limitations) the lower is the cost per piece.

But in deciding the quantity of pieces to be operated upon at one setting, the other commitments of the machine must not be overlooked, for the weekly output of the machining department as a whole must consist of complete sets of components, and not 1,000 of one, 280 of another, and none of a third. And one machine (except in very special cases) is not wholly concerned with one component part; two or three, or perhaps a dozen, different parts must be handled on one specific machine and this must receive consideration.

Two factors, therefore, decide the quantity of each part to be operated upon at one setting, viz. a time allowance that will mean economical production, and the period for which the machine can be given over to one specific component part, having regard to other commitments. Thus, a standard quantity is fixed, and this is duly scheduled, so that this quantity figures on all works orders. The time allowance is based upon this quantity, and then calculated per piece, for convenience, thus: Time allowance for 500 pieces $= 3\frac{3}{4}$ hours $= \cdot45$ minute each.

The operation sheet (or route card) details all operations necessary to transform the material into a finished component part, but operation planning must continue beyond this. It may be that the piece, although known as a finished component part, is not completed until joined with another part, as, for example, an endshield with a split cap. The endshield is known by one part number and the cap by another, but when the two come together the endshield complete is known by a third part number. One operation sheet, therefore, details the operations associated with the endshield proper, one the operations associated with the cap, whilst a third carries on with the operations necessary to transform the endshield and cap into a complete endshield.

The matter is carried still farther by a process of sub-assembling, the idea being to bring together as many loose parts as possible, so that the final erection of the unit comprises the connecting up of a number of complete assemblies. The unit itself may be comprised of 100 different component parts, but on account of sub-assembling no more than, say, thirty loose parts are handled in the final erection. This sub-assembling forms a test of operation planning, as efficiency here means economy in manufacture. Each sub-assembly is separately treated, and has its own operation sheet. Practical illustrations showing this phase of manufacture in greater detail are to be found in the succeeding chapter.

We have now reached the termination of the planner's activities, for henceforth others must take the lead. The planner has prepared the ground and sowed the seed, but care and attention must not be relaxed if we are to secure a good harvest. To all intents and purposes, conditions are favourable; the field is well cultivated and the seed is good. So long as the birds refrain from eating our growth; so long as the weeds refrain from encumbering the field, our harvest should be good, given sunshine and rain at the times required. But, unless precautions are taken, the birds will feed and the weeds will grow, whilst climatic conditions may prove unfavourable. The farmer cannot afford to rely upon his initial effort and rest from spring-time till autumn, neither can the factory afford to rely wholly upon the activities of the planner, without taking the necessary steps to ensure the maximum results from those activities. The planner has said that certain things can be done, and it is for someone to see that they *are* done. This is accomplished through the medium of a routeing system, devised to exploit the ideas of the planner, and how this is done is given in the next chapter.

CHAPTER V

ROUTEING SYSTEMS AND CONTROL BOARDS

To carry on the work of the planner with any degree of success it is necessary to establish a department which is wholly and solely concerned with works routine. This is the progress (or routeing) department, and no matter how large or how small the factory may be—no matter by what methods manufacture is handled—it is certain that, without this department, the results of even the most careful planning will be disappointing.

The functions of the progress department vary in the different factories, according to the range of manufacture and the general system prevailing, whilst even in the type of factory similar to the one under review, which is interested in but one class of apparatus manufactured on repetition lines, the views of the management on the functions of this department show some diversity. In some factories the planner is expected to assume responsibility not only for the actual planning, but also for the carrying out of the work which will ensure the realization of that planning. When this is the case, the routeing department is but a section of the planning department, simply carrying on in accordance with the instructions of the planner but displaying no initiative.

This is what may be termed "office control," which gets results by an automatic process. It is contended by those in favour that the method *must* be efficient—that as every move has been scientifically planned, and it is known that a certain result is possible, the possibility *must* become a certainty. The experience of the writer, however, forces him to the conclusion that "office control" never did, and never will, secure the maximum results, and even in factories where the method finds favour, the personal intervention of one official or another is necessary to speed up the "automatic process" in order to get somewhere near the "proved capacity of the factory."

And in this "personal intervention" lies the crux of the argument—whether it shall be an unknown quantity or part of a systematized campaign. The unknown quantity is unsatisfactory because it hides so many vital factors—the direct cost of the intervention, the indirect cost, and the real cause of the trouble. Direct cost is not known because it is covered by the general supervisory expense—one foreman may quietly visit another for the purpose of speeding up supplies—the works manager may have to spend a good deal of time in the manufacturing departments to consider how to deal with an emergency—the planning department may send a clerk to various foremen with a view to securing information. (This latter, by the way, comes perilously near to "progress chasing," which is condemned by many exponents of "office control.") Indirect cost cannot be ascertained because it is not known how much the efficiency of the department suffers on account of the absence of the foreman, nor what is lost owing to the works manager's neglect of other duties to provide the time he has to spend in the shops. The real cause of the trouble is unknown because in some instances the trouble itself never comes to the ears of the management, whilst in others all efforts are directed toward overcoming the trouble, and no time is available for inquiring into the cause.

It is far better to have the known quantity as an integral part of the organization, and thus frankly recognize the value of progress work. And this, to be effective, must be independent of the control of the planning office—the planner has prepared the ground, and now the progressman must do his part. We will first give the details of a scheme that "goes the whole hog," and then consider an alternative scheme that limits to some extent the activities of the progressman, and which may be deemed more suitable for certain types of factories.

As the Route Cards (Fig. 14) are made out by the planner, they are sent to the progress office (which is situated in a convenient and easily accessible part of the workshop) and are filed in a box in consecutive part number order. In course of time there is one card for every component part comprising a given unit, and this set of cards contains all the information needed by the progressman to put into process of manufacture all parts associated with that unit. So when an order is received from the management to put in hand 1,000 type Y units, the route card for each component part shows the section and amount of material required; particulars of each operation in the correct sequence; the machine or station upon

ROUTE CARD

Made out by ....A. W. C. Date.......21/8/..........
Checked by ....W. J. H. Date.......21/8/..........

Part No.......483.

Description.......Centre Wheel..........
Material or Symbol.......1⅜" dia. × 14G Brass Strip..........

Standard Quantity.......500..........
Standard Amount.......68 ft...........

Operation No.	Operation	Machine No. or Station No.	Grade of Labour	Jigs and Fixtures	Tools	Setting Time	Time Allowed (mins. each)	Time to complete Std. Quan.
1	Blank and pierce	33	2	J/15/483		½ hr.	·33	2¾ hrs.
2	Flatten	34	3				·66	5½ "
3	Rough grain	80/85	3				·3	2½ "
4	Turn-cutting dia.	71/74	2				·6	5 "
5	Cut	43	1			1¼ hrs.	1·09	9 "
6	Bore	91	1				2·5	20¾ "
7	Finish grain	80/85	1				2·0	16¾ "
	For Sub-assembly	A12						

FIG. 14

which each operation must be handled; the time allowed for each operation, etc.

Upon receipt of the order, the progressman must, in the first instance, ascertain what supplies of raw materials are available, and with this end in view he consults a card record, known as the Balance Record of Raw Materials (see Fig. 15), and enters into the appropriate columns the amount of material to be allocated or reserved, noting how this affects the stocks and placing a requisition upon the buying department for such extra supplies as are necessary. It may be contrary to the policy of the firm to hold heavy surplus stocks of materials, but in requisitioning further supplies it will be well to order somewhat in excess of the actual requirement as shown upon the route card, to meet an emergency occasioned by heavy scrapping, or a special rush order, etc. It may be well to state that the planner has been generous in his estimate, taking into consideration wastage likely to be caused by short ends, faulty pieces, etc., but even so the amount requisitioned (allowing, of course, for what is actually in stock) should exceed the estimated amount by at least 10 per cent, whilst in many cases the margin should be even greater.

The progress office must keep in touch with the buyer in regard to material on order, sending reminders from time to time, with a view to speeding up delivery. To render it unnecessary for the progressman to peruse every card weekly in order to ascertain what material is outstanding, a classified list is compiled at the time of requisitioning, upon which the various items are recorded. One list gives particulars of round steel bar ordered, another gives particulars of brass strip, and so on, whilst items which are few in number and cannot readily be classified appear on one list under the heading of "Miscellaneous." One of these classified lists is illustrated by Fig. 16.

The question of material being settled, the issue of operation job orders is the next item for consideration, and in this connection the first thing to be decided upon is the quantity to be covered by each job order. It will be remembered that a works order has been received covering 1,000 units, which means that at least 1,000 of each component part must be manufactured, this number being increased if two, three, or four details to one specific part number are required for each unit.

BALANCE RECORD OF RAW MATERIALS

Description.................... Sheet Iron 6' × 3' .... Bin or Stores No.................. A 20..................

Material or Symbol.................. 16G.................. When Balance in Stock falls below......56 lb.......re-order......500 lb..................

Quantity Requisitioned on Buyer			Quantity Allocated		Balance	Quantity Received in Stores			Quantity Issued to Shops				Balance Actually	Reserve	
Req. No.	Date	Quantity	Job No.	Quantity	Available	Insp. Note No.	Date	Quantity	Req. No.	Job No.	Date	Quantity	In Stock	Job No.	Quantity
1476	25/8/....	560 lb.	1117 to 1120	500 lb.	60 lb.	1373	30/8/....	560 lb.	124	1117	1/9/....	125 lb.	435 lb.		
									125	1118	"	125 lb.	310 lb.		
			1410	30 lb.	30 lb.				130	119	4/9	125 lb.	185 lb.		
1490	5/9	560 lb.							131	120	"	125 lb.	60 lb.	1410	30 lb.

FIG. 15

CLASSIFIED LIST OF MATERIAL ON ORDER WITH OUTSIDE FIRMS

BAR STEEL.

For Order No.	Requisition No.	Date	Amount	Particulars	Purchasing Order No.	Dated	Due	Received
595	1415	15/7/....	10 cwt.	$\frac{1}{2}$" dia. Brt.	3853	21/7/....	28/7/...	1/8/....
617	1423	21/7	1 ton	1" dia. M.S.	4111	26/7	31/7	
630	1431	28/7	5 cwt.	$\frac{3}{16}$" dia. Brt.	4120	30/7		
633	1432	30/7	1 ton	$\frac{3}{4}$" dia. M.S.	4137	8/8		
650	1500	10/8	10 cwt.	$\frac{7}{16}$" dia. M.S.				

FIG. 16

It may be that in some instances the whole number required can be accommodated on one job number, but in other cases, when the operation is of a lengthy character, it is desirable to split the number, so that one machine or operator is not engaged on one job for a long period, whilst other jobs are delayed. In some factories the procedure of having "unfinished orders" is favoured; in other words, an order covering 1,000 pieces is issued and worked upon, but when 250 of these pieces are completed the job is stopped and another order is given to the operator, the original order being again picked up at a future date, and a further supply of parts completed in accordance with this.

The object of the scheme under review is to obviate the necessity for "unfinished orders," by making the quantity in each case small enough to permit of completion at one setting, whilst being large enough to ensure economical manufacture. Thus, the requirement of 1,000 pieces is covered by two orders of 500 each, four orders of 250 each, five orders of 200 each, or maybe ten orders of 100 each. It is understood that the longest operation forms the basis of division, although this operation may be toward the end of the sequence. For example, the time allowance may be low enough on the first three operations for each of these to be covered by one job order, whilst operation No. 4 may necessitate the issue of two orders, and operation No. 5 four orders. When this is the case four job numbers are allotted, but a system of grouping is permissible in the case of the earlier operations. To illustrate this more fully we will assume that for 1,000 pieces to a certain part number the four job orders allotted are Nos. 101, 102, 103, 104. Each of the first three operations can be covered by one order, and the number appearing on this order is 101–2–3–4. Operation No. 4 necessitates the issue of two orders, numbered respectively 101–102, and 103–104, whilst the four orders issued to cover operation No. 5 are numbered 101, 102, 103, 104 respectively. It is understood that, once this division has been effected, re-grouping cannot be resorted to in connection with subsequent operations, even though the time allowed for these operations is low enough to permit the full quantity to be handled on one order.

The splitting up of the quantity for the purposes of manufacture is recorded in a Job Order Register, illustrated by Fig. 17. This may be continuous, which means that job orders are numbered

Form..................
Date..................

JOB ORDER REGISTER

W.O. No.	Chart No.	Job No.	Description	Part No.	Quantity	Ent. Form 8, Columns 7, 8, 9, & 14	J.O. Form 5 made out by	J.O. Card Comp. No. Good	J.O. Card Comp. Card to Cost
112		32	Barrel Tube	4	250		H	240	3/7/....
		33	Barrel Cap	5	250		H		
		34	,,	5	250		H		
		35	,,	5	250		H		
		36	,,	5	250		H		
		37	,,	5	250		H		
		38	Barrel Tube Rivet	6	500		H	500	28/5/....
		39	,,	6	500		H	510	28/5/....

FIG. 17

consecutively, and assigned to any part number about to be put into process, or a certain series of job numbers may be reserved for a given part number, which means that, whenever that part is to be put into process, the job order must bear one of the reserved numbers, as, for example, the job order issued for part No. 5 must bear the Nos. 32, 34, 35, 36, or 37.

The latter method certainly saves a good deal of clerical work, for when a new works order is received a strip of paper (suitably printed) can be pasted over the previous entries (from the quantity column to the end) and then the necessary details can be filled in.

After the register has been compiled, the clerk enters all job orders relating to a specific component upon the Component Progress Record, illustrated by Fig. 18, and when in course of time the various operation cards are made out, the numbers also appear upon this card. The record is filed under the part number, and its object is to show at a glance the total number of orders placed, and the precise whereabouts of the parts covered by any of these orders. How this record is completed will be shown later when dealing with the routine covering work in progress.

The Detail Chart (Fig. 19) is next compiled, and in regard to this it may be said that it can be made large enough to cover 2,000 or even more units, so that it will not be necessary to draft out a new chart for every works order received. It will be noted that all component parts comprising the unit are listed, and in such a way as to show the various sub-assemblies leading up to final erection. A perusal of the chart illustrated shows that the first three items cover details which, when machined, can be assembled together, and item 4 shows this sub-assembly. Items 5 and 6 cover two more details which, together with the previous assembly, in turn form another assembly, shown on item 7. The next three items cover further details, and these, assembled with the parts covered by item 7, complete the assembly, in which condition the parts are held in stock pending the final erection of the unit. The item covering the last assembly in each instance is entered in red, whilst for all other items black ink is used. The reason for this will be explained later.

The horizontal lines opposite to each item are for recording progress, the first line in each instance (in red) denoting that material is available and the first operation order issued, whilst

COMPONENT PROGRESS RECORD

Description .... Part No. ....

Material .... Standard Quantity ....

Standard Amount ....

Works Order No.	Amount		Material from Store		Machine No.____ Operation No.____ Operation ____			Machine No.____ Operation No.____ Operation ____			Machine No.____ Operation No.____ Operation ____			Machine No.____ Operation No.____ Operation ____			Machine No.____ Operation No.____ Operation ____		
	Quan.	Material	Reqn. No.	Date	Clock Card No.	Date Complete	Quan. Good	Clock Card No.	Date Complete	Quan. Good	Clock Card No.	Date Complete	Quan. Good	Clock Card No.	Date Complete	Quan. Good	Clock Card No.	Date Complete	Quan. Good

NOTE.—When final operation is completed, enter up F.C. Stock Card.

FIG. 18

the bottom line in each instance (in black) denotes that all operations are completed. Thus, looking at item 1 on the chart, we see that material is available and the first operation order issued for 300 sets, and that of these 250 sets have been completed, leaving fifty sets still in progress. The whereabouts of this fifty sets can be ascertained by referring to the Component Progress Record No. 5,121 (Fig. 18).

Now we come to the making out of the operator's job card, which is designed for use in connection with an automatic time recorder. The card (see Fig. 20) is of the folding variety, and perforated to permit the detachment. When folded, carbon paper can be used for duplicating the initial entries, which are as follows: (a) Machine No.; (b) Clock Card No. (placed by a multistamp); (c) Job Order No.; (d) Quantity; (e) Part No.; (f) Description; (g) Operation No.; (h) Operation. These particulars are obtained from the Component Progress Record (Fig. 18), whilst the other entries (which are not duplicated), viz. grade of labour and time allowance, are obtained from the Route Card.

The same job order number is used in connection with all operations associated with a specific quantity, and this is used for the purposes of identification and also for costing. The items referring to order number and name of department, at the top of the card on the extreme left of the diagram, are filled in by the clerk, but the particulars relating to operator's name and number, also the week ending date, are entered by the foreman when the operation is about to be put in hand.

A card for every operation is made out by the clerk in the first instance, the quantity being omitted except in the case of the first operation. At this juncture the Control Board (see Fig. 21) comes up for review. This is a double-sided board furnished with pockets, so arranged that four pockets appear under each machine number, in vertical form. The pocket immediately beneath the machine number is for the card covering the job actually in hand, the one below for the card covering the next job to be put in hand, the third for the cards relating to jobs for which material is available, and the last for cards covering the jobs for which at the moment no material is available. It may be observed that, whereas pockets numbered 1 and 2 will ordinarily accommodate but one card each at a time, pockets 3 and 4 will accommodate a much larger number.

When the clerk has made out all operation cards relating to one specific job order, all cards are at once placed in the bottom pocket of the machines designated, with the exception of the card relating to the first operation which (if the material is available) is placed in pocket No. 3.

Having thus observed the means whereby operation orders are made out, we may now deal with the procedure for the issue and return of operation card, and the means by which progress is recorded. The exact order of precedence in the matter of issues is determined by the progressman, who uses the Detail Chart (Fig. 19) as a guide. But it sometimes happens that circumstances will not permit this programme to be rigidly adhered to—there may be a shortage of material or trouble with tools—and when this is the case a substitute job must be selected, in order that the machine may be fully employed.

Dealing with "first operations," the material for which must come from the store, the clerk can ascertain if this material is available by reference to the Raw Material Record. If reference reveals the fact that there is insufficient material available, the operation card is placed in No. 4 pocket, but if material is available, a requisition for the amount desired is made out, and attached to the operation card, which is placed in pocket No. 3. The progressman can, by glancing at the Control Board, see the number of jobs for which material is available, and can arrange these in the order he desires, using detachable signals to denote the order of precedence.

When a first operation job is about to be put in progress (it being remarked that there is already one job on the machine) the card is taken from pocket No. 3 and detached where perforated, the portion containing the "clocking columns," to which the material requisition is attached, being sent to the department foreman, whilst the other half of the card is placed in pocket No. 2, as showing "the next job on." In course of time the job already in operation is completed, and the operator brings to the process office the corresponding job card and also the job card covering the next job. The first is "clocked off" as completed, and the second is "clocked on," the corresponding cards on the control board being moved thus: The card in pocket No. 1 is removed, as this covers the job just completed, and is placed in a box marked "Inspection," whilst the card reposing in pocket No. 2 is removed to pocket

No. 1, this denoting that a new job has been put in hand. As soon as possible after this, one of the cards from pocket No. 3 is dealt with in the manner just described, one half being sent to the department foreman and the other half placed in pocket No. 2.

When the operator has clocked "off and on," he deposits the work (with his card) in the inspection department, which is adjacent to the progress office. He then draws the material from store in accordance with the requisition, and commences work upon his new order. The inspector, in the meantime, examines the details submitted to him, and makes a record of his findings upon the job card in the appropriate columns, and when this is done the details, together with the job card, are passed to the man in charge of the "work in progress" store.

This man receives and issues all batches of work in progress, his authority in each case being the job card, which accompanies all work received in the store, and which must be presented before work can be taken from the store. When a batch of work is received in the store from the inspection department, it is placed by the storekeeper in a bin or on a shelf, and the number or symbol of this bin or shelf is entered in pencil on the job card.

It will be remembered that the other half of the job card has for some time been reposing in a box labelled "inspection," but as the job has now left the inspection department, this card must be removed. The removal is accomplished by the storekeeper, who thus brings the two halves of the card together and hands them to the progress clerk. It is, of course, obvious that each job is not dealt with separately, as the storekeeper is continually receiving details and cards; the pairing of the latter is therefore done at frequent intervals and handed to the clerk in batches.

When completed operation job cards are received, the first duty of the clerk is to enter upon the "office" half the particulars entered upon the operator's card by the inspector and the storekeeper, and when this has been done the operator's card is placed in the "outgoing" basket for delivery to the wages office. The corresponding card is first used for entering up the Component Progress Record (Fig. 11), and then as a means for putting into process the next operation, in the following manner.

The card gives the job number and also the number of the machine upon which the next operation is to be handled. The clerk goes to the control board, and takes from the bottom pocket under the machine number given the operation job card bearing the same job number as the card just dealt with. Upon this new card is entered the bin or shelf number and also the quantity completed on the previous operation, and the card is then placed in pocket No. 3, denoting that material is available. The previous operation card, now completed, is filed for reference.

When, in course of time, the second operation is about to be handled, the operator's card is presented to the storekeeper, who forthwith issues the necessary material. The fact that the bin or shelf number appears upon this card obviates wasted time in this connection, as the material is speedily located.

The procedure given above governs the issue of all operation job cards and also the returns to the work in progress store, until the return takes the form of a finished component part. Then the card, instead of bearing a shelf or bin number, is indorsed "clearance," and the parts are housed in the "clearance" section of the store, until such time as they are reissued in connection with a subassembly. Also, the return of a finished component part varies the procedure in the progress office, for in addition to the duties already mentioned, the clerk must enter the return upon a Finished Component Part Card (Fig. 22) and show by means of a black line on the Detail Chart (Fig. 19) the quantity of parts completed.

A glance at the Detail Chart just referred to shows the progressman whether sufficient completed component parts are available to allow him to put sub-assemblies into operation. Assuming that there is a sufficiency of parts, he consults the component progress record bearing the part number of the sub-assembly, and ascertains from this the number on the control board under which the first operation job card is to be found. To this card he attaches a schedule, giving particulars of the parts comprising the sub-assembly, and hands it to the storekeeper for execution. The latter gets the parts together from the "clearance" section, and places them in a bin reserved for work in progress, entering the bin number upon the job card in the manner already described. The job card and the schedule are then handed to the progress clerk, who places the former in the appropriate pocket (No. 3) on the control board, and uses the schedule for posting issues on the finished component part card. When the sub-assembly is completed and

FINISHED COMPONENT STOCK

DESCRIPTION................Ratchet...................   PART NO...........436...............

QUANTITY TO ORDER..........100...............

In Progress			Received into Store			In Store	Issues for Assembly			Stock
Date	Order No.	Quantity	Date	Order No.	Quantity	Quantity	Date	Order No.	Quantity	Balance in Stores
8/3	2314	100	21/4	2314	99	99	27/3	1577	20	79
31/3	2581	100					29/3	1578	40	39
							31/3	1581	10	29

FIG. 22

Job Number . .		3120	3121	3122	3124	3130	3171	3172	3173	3190	3191
Date Issued . .		12/3/_	12/3/_	12/3/_	22/3/_	29/3/_	20/4/_	20/4/_	20/4/_	4/5/_	4/5/_

Part No.	Description	No. per Set	10	20	30	40	50	60	70	80	90	100
A605	Barrel . .	1	10	10	10	10	10	10	10	10	10	10
A510	Centre Pinion .	1	10	10	10	10	10	10	10	10	10	10
A511	Inter Pinion .	1	10	10	10	10	10	10	10	10	10	10
A512	Regulator Nut	2	20	20	20	20	20	20	20	20	20	20
A516	Warning Pinion	1	10	10	10	10	10	10	10	10	10	10
A520	Rack . .	1	10	10	10	10	10	10	10	10	10	10
A523	Pulley Wheel .	2	20	20	20	20	20	20	20	20	20	20
A524	Third Pinion .	1	10	10	10	10	10	10	10	10	10	10
A528	Maintaining Rod . .	2	20	20	20	20	20	20	20	20	20	20
A530	Bridge . .	1	10	10	10	10	10	10	10	10	10	10
A533	Fly Wheel .	1	10	10	10	10	10	10	10	10	10	10
509	Main Wheel .	1	10	10	10	10	10	10	10	10	10	10
513	Ratchet . .	1	10	10	10	10	10	10	10	10	10	10
514	Spring . .	1	10	10	10	10	10	10	10	10	10	10
515	Screw . .	1	10	10	10	10	10	10	10	10	10	10
517	Nut . .	1	10	10	10	10	10	10	10	10	10	10
518	Crutch . .	1	10	10	10	10	10	10	10	10	10	10
519	Pillar . .	4	40	40	40	40	40	40	40	40	40	40
521	Pillar Nut .	4	40	40	40	40	40	40	40	40	40	40
522	Pillar Washer .	4	40	40	40	40	40	40	40	40	40	40
525	Socket . .	2	20	20	20	20	20	20	20	20	20	20
526	Plate (front) .	1	10	10	10	10	10	10	10	10	10	10
527	Plate (back) .	1	10	10	10	10	10	10	10	10	10	10

3192	3201	3210	3211	3226	3227	3250	3251												
4/5/_	7/6/_	18/6/_	18/6/_	30/6/_	30/6/_														
110	120	130	140	150	160	170	180	190	200	210	220	230	240	250	260	270	280	290	300
10	10	10	10	10	6														
10	10	10	10	10	10	10	10												
10	10	10	10	10	10														
20	20	20	20	20	20	20	20												
10	10	10	10	10	10	10	10												
10	10	10	10	10	10	10	10												
20	20	20	20	20	20	20	20												
10	10	10	10	10	10	10	4												
20	20	20	20	20	20	20	20												
10	10	10	10	10	10														
10	10	10	10	10	8														
10	10	10	10	10	10	10	10												
10	10	10	10	10	10	10	10												
10	10	10	10	10	10	10	10												
10	10	10	10	10	10	10	10												
10	10	10	10	10	10	10	10												
10	10	10	10	10	10	10	10												
40	40	40	40	40	40	40	40												
40	40	40	40	40	40	40	40												
40	40	40	40	40	40	40	40												
20	20	20	20	20	20	20	20												
10	10	10	10	10	10	10	10												
10	10	10	10	10	10	10	10												

FIG. 23

returned to the store it is placed in the "clearance" section, and the procedure given above is followed in connection with all sub-assemblies until the one just prior to the final erection of the unit is completed, when it is placed in the finished part stores.

When the parts are to be collected for the final erection of the unit a chart similar to Fig. 23 is used. This gives particulars of all separate parts comprising the unit, those with the letter A before the part number being completed sub-assemblies. The chart is divided into squares for the accommodation of the number of units to be assembled on the various job orders, the number selected for the purposes of illustration being ten.

The best method to follow in connection with the assembling of completed units is for the various parts to be collected together some time prior to their actual requirement, as this gives the progress man early knowledge of a possible shortage. It is, of course, easy for him to refer to the detail chart and see what parts are lagging behind, but there is more significance in the information derived from the assembling chart, for here it is abundantly clear that the shortage of a certain part is actually preventing the completion of an assembling batch. And if he knows this week what is short on the batches required by the assemblers next week, he can commence to speed up early enough to permit the lagging parts being available when required.

With this end in view, further sets of parts are collected together before the immediately preceding sets are sent to the assembling shop, and if there is a shortage, the blank squares will bring this prominently to the fore. As finished parts are received in the store, the storekeeper appropriates the quantity required for the batches, and marks up the chart accordingly. It has been the writer's practice always to have a shortage upon the chart, as a means of stimulating the actions of the progress man, the method being to batch up further sets of parts immediately the chart recorded "no shortage," even though these further sets would not be required for some little time.

When a batch of parts is about to be sent to the assemblers, the various details are brought out and checked with the chart, the progress man calling out the items and the storekeeper counting the parts into a box. This goes a long way towards ensuring accuracy, as the overlooking of any item in the initial collection is brought to notice by this method. An operator's job card is selected, and the number entered upon the chart in the appropriate column, the date being placed immediately beneath this number as shown on the diagram.

One other point needs to be discussed in connection with this system, this referring to the recording of scrap and subsequent replacements. In most factories a certain proportion of operation orders shows a percentage of scrap incurred in manufacture, and the fact that this percentage is usually very low may suggest to the management that it is not worth bothering about. But it has to be remembered that "a lot of littles makes a lot," and the two's and three's, when multiplied by the 50 or 100 job orders which go through the shops in the space of six months, grow into a formidable quantity, which is reflected in the finished parts record, unless action is taken to replace.

It is obvious that replacement orders cannot be issued to cover the scrap made on each job order, unless action is delayed until the quantity necessitating replacement is large enough to ensure economy in manufacture. Some firms endeavour to obviate the necessity for replacement orders by increasing the quantity on each first operation job order beyond the actual requirement; that is to say, if the requirement is 200 pieces, the quantity to be made is fixed at 220, so that, should any number up to twenty be scrapped during manufacture, the requirement can still be met.

This may answer in many cases, but immunity from replacement orders cannot be guaranteed, and the following appears to be the better method. All operation job cards are perused by the progress clerk before being sent to the wages office, and a record made of all the scrap appearing thereon. The record, known as the Scrap Register (and illustrated by Fig. 24), is designed to facilitate the summarizing of all scrap associated with a specific part number, so that it is an easy matter to determine when a replacement order is due. Every week the progress man consults this register, and gives instructions for the issue of certain replacement orders, his decisions being based upon (a) an economical working number having been reached, or (b) the knowledge that similar parts on a productive order are about to be put in hand. In regard to the latter, the question of quantity is by no means pronounced, for if an order is about to be put in hand covering 200 parts, a replacement order for twenty at this juncture would be more economical than one for 100 a little later, for obvious reasons.

When a replacement order is issued, particulars are entered in red in the first vacant square, it being understood that the whole of the scrap recorded in the preceding squares is covered by the replacement. Subsequent scrap is recorded in the manner described in the illustration, and this continues until the quantity again suggests the necessity for a replacement order. In this manner a strict check is kept upon all scrap, and there is no fear of replacements being overlooked, or of quantities being placed on order for impossible numbers, from a manufacturing standpoint.

Provided it is in capable hands and properly worked, the routeing system just described will give satisfactory results, for not only will it carry planning to its logical conclusion, but it will also ensure that smooth working necessary to get the maximum of efficiency from the manufacturing departments. Many a good planning scheme has been spoiled by faulty application brought about by the "cheese-paring" policy of the management in regard to progress work, for "expense" here is regarded with aversion, and the personnel is quite inadequate. The difficulties of the small manufacturer are fully appreciated by the author, but he suggests that in far too many instances the "economy axe" is injudiciously applied. Where waste abounds it is allowed to continue, because it is strongly entrenched, and the "economy axe" comes down where resistance is weak. It is farcical to expend time and ingenuity on perfecting a planning system, and then spoil all for the sake of saving a pound a week.

It is difficult to review a scheme in detail without making it appear formidable, and maybe many readers will consider the scheme given above too formidable for the small factory. To allay any apprehensions which may be felt on this score, the following may be of interest. A routeing system, similar to the one outlined, was handled by a staff of five, viz. a progress man, three girl clerks, and a youth acting as storekeeper. Before the scheme was in operation, the administrative staff of the factory (apart from the supervisory staff) consisted of a progress man, one girl clerk, a girl acting as a storekeeper, and a youth. The activities of these people were so disconnected that the percentage of efficiency was deplorably low, and production suffered accordingly. With the same staff (plus one) properly organized, and working in a systematic manner upon a pre-determined plan, the output from the manufacturing departments increased in a remarkable manner, this proving that co-ordinated routine is far more effective than individualistic effort.

At the commencement of this chapter we spoke of an alternative scheme, less ambitious in its scope, which might appeal to those who are not prepared to organize on the lines suggested. Such a scheme may now be described, it being observed that certain of the details are uniform with those already expounded.

The chief difference in the two schemes is that, in the one about to be reviewed, a recognized planning department is not in existence. Operation planning is, in the first instance, handled by the production manager, and a rate fixer is engaged for setting times. The operations and times are set out on a standard schedule, but the allotment of the job to the machine is not covered by this.

A works order for a given number of completed units is received in the progress office, and immediately all first operation job cards are made out by the clerk. To each is attached a requisition on the store for the material required, and the job card and the requisition are sent to the store, a duplicate of each remaining in the progress office. Upon receipt, the storekeeper allots material to the job order, marking the order accordingly, which is then sent to the foreman handling the operation. If there is insufficient material available, a requisition is put through to the purchasing office for further supplies, and the job card is retained in the store until these supplies are received, when it is marked and sent to the foreman concerned.

It must be made clear that material does not accompany the job card to the foreman, as this must be applied for. The fact that a foreman has a marked job card in his possession proves that material is available upon demand, and when the job is about to be put in hand the job card is presented at the store, and the necessary material obtained.

In the progress office there is a Control Chart similar to the one illustrated by Fig. 25, upon which all machine numbers are shown. Cross sections are shown to represent every working hour of the day, the whole being designed to serve for a forty-seven hour week. The object of this chart is to ensure every machine being fully employed throughout the week, by showing the job in hand and when it was started, the follow-up job, and so on. The method employed is as follows.

Assuming for the moment that we have a clean chart for the week, and that we are dealing with a machine handling first operations only, the foreman selects from among the marked job cards in his possession one to be put into operation. This is taken to the store in the first instance by a labourer, and the necessary material obtained, the card and the material then being handed to the operator. At the same time the foreman selects a "follow-up" job, and may be a third, according to the time allowance on each, the idea being to map out the work for each machine at least a week ahead. These cards are likewise handed to the operator, each marked in order of precedence, but material is not drawn from stores until the job is about to be put in hand.

From this point the procedure is somewhat similar to that already described. The operator takes the first job card to the progress office and is "clocked on" the job, whilst the remaining cards are noted in the progress office and returned to the operator, who places them on a rack in his own section until one is required for putting in hand. At frequent intervals the operator's racks are inspected by the foreman, who makes further selections of jobs as required, the selected cards being presented at the progress office for noting at the earliest opportunity. When the job in hand is completed the card is "clocked off" and the card for the next job "clocked on," as before described.

When jobs are presented at the progress office, the duplicates are pinned to the control chart in the following order. The time allowed on the job taken in hand is calculated from the time of "clocking on," and the duplicate affixed to the chart at the hour by which the job should be completed. The second job card is affixed at the hour by which the job should be completed, based upon the first calculation. In other words, if the first job is "clocked on" at 9.30 a.m. on 23rd July, and the time allowed is 10½ hours, the position of the card upon the chart is on the line 11.30 a.m. on 24th July. The follow-up job allowance is four hours, which means that the card for this job is on the line 4.30 p.m. on the same date.

This method not only shows that every machine is employed,

but it also shows at a glance when any machine will be free, a most important matter in some factories. It may be contended that it is a difficut matter to calculate the times correctly, as the time allowed is not necessarily the time taken, but the trouble here can be overcome as the scheme develops. At the outset, it is necessary to take the time allowed as the basis, as there is no other standard, but after a while the actual time taken is easily determined, and can then be used as a standard, 25 per cent or 33⅓ per cent being deducted for the purpose of making the calculations more in keeping with actualities.

The chart can be made a permanent feature, the only adjustments being in connection with the date column. This is in the form of a frame into which cards bearing the date can be slipped. When the top portion of the chart (representing the earlier portion of the week) is free, dates for the following week can at once be inserted, and to prevent any confusion these may be written in a different colour ink.

When a job is completed, the card is taken from the chart, and the card covering the new job is adjusted, if necessary, this meaning that, if the first job is completed earlier (or later) than calculated, a corresponding movement must be made in connection with the next card, it being understood that the position of the card representing the job in hand is determined by the actual time of clocking on, plus the time allowed.

Job cards covering second and all subsequent operations are not made out until the card covering the preceding operation is received in the progress office as completed. These cards bear a requisition on the work in progress store for the necessary parts, and the procedure of the foreman is the same as in the case of first operations. The recording of work in progress, etc., is in this instance substantially the same as that already described.

It is understood that the method of routeing varies considerably in different factories, and neither of the two systems given may altogether commend itself to the reader. It is not the desire of the writer to assert that they cannot be improved upon, but he does believe that one or the other can be accepted in principle by any factory manager, and modified to suit his own requirements. Whatever method is favoured, however, it must be applied with thoroughness, and every contingency provided against. There is perhaps no need to say that both the schemes given have been worked by the writer, who has drafted them out, not in their original form, but with the modifications he considered necessary to make in order to apply them effectively in connection with the work he had on hand.

PART II— PROGRESS WORK

CHAPTER VI

THE "PROGRESS" IDEA

THE "progress" idea has taken root in this country, and it is growing fast. Held exclusively for many years by the large and wealthy concerns, it has during the last decade been exploited by the manufacturer of more moderate means, and now the small man is invoking its aid. No longer is its adoption delayed on the score of expense, for this is an exploded fallacy, and to-day it is being commended for its effectiveness—and cheapness.

It is no longer monopolized by the large concern, for it is open to all who are enlightened enough to understand the principle. It is no longer monopolized by the engineering industry, for its advantages are to-day appreciated by manufacturers of leather, soap, and paint (to name but a few), and its application to these manufactures is as successful as it is to the various branches of the engineering industry.

Wherever manufacture is comprised of specialized processes and operations (and in these days, what manufacture is not?) the application of the progress idea is necessary to ensure success. We may devise, scheme, and plan—all upon scientific lines—and vouch for the accuracy of our findings; but to expect 100 per cent efficiency without the agency of the progress idea is as bad as the inventor endeavouring to place his product upon the market without developing a commercial organization to exploit it.

The progress idea "fastens" upon the planning result as something possible—something probable—but something uncertain, and it proceeds to knock off the negative prefix. In other words, the planning result is gently but firmly directed into its proper channel, shielded from the adverse factors inseparable from actual application, and is given the opportunity to demonstrate in practice the soundness of the theory.

True, this is nothing but routine, but it is routine that mars or makes the venture. The man who "plans" an operation knows that it *can* be handled on a certain machine, that it *can* be completed in a given time, but it is the progress idea which ensures that it *will* be. Left to itself, the planning result makes but little headway, but taken in hand by the progress idea, it becomes a scientific force, and as such is the basis of modern manufacture.

The value of the progress idea was first recognized by the engineering industry, and followed the sectionizing of departments and the dissecting of operations. The logical outcome was the creation of a department to materialize the idea, and to-day there is scarcely an engineering factory of repute in the country without a recognized progress department. True, many of these "progress departments" are but caricatures of the real thing, and must needs be reconstructed before they can function successfully; but the fact that they are in existence is proof that the idea is accepted as the medium for ensuring the practicability of planning.

The large engineering concern has an elaborate progress organization—the small concern one of more simple construction, but presumably proportionate to the need. That in some factories the progress department is inefficient is sometimes due to the fact that the need has been under-estimated—hence the department is overwhelmed. The general factory routine may call for a vast amount of clerical work, which must be reduced if it is to be handled by a small staff. Of what use are records which are never up to date? Yet upon these time is being spent which could be more profitably employed elsewhere! In one factory the works manager was proud of his production chart, yet the figures on that chart were often two weeks in arrears, a sad state of affairs for a presumably well-organized factory.

If the record (or the chart) is regarded as essential by the management, the necessary time must be spent upon it to keep it up to date, but it is folly to insist upon the inclusion of such a record when that which it portrays is quite valueless. It is this sort of thing that causes the manager, the foreman, and the workman, to rail against the "system"—not realizing that it is the application, and not the system, which is at fault.

The "system" does not insist upon the inclusion of that precise record—its inclusion is the outcome of the management's interpretation of the principle of the system, which interpretation may be quite correct in the sense that no satisfactory alternative can be devised. The record in question may relate to the available stocks of raw materials, which must be posted daily to be of any real value, but there are other records which are presumably of more importance, because they are more often referred to by the higher authorities. In the understaffed progress office, is it not logical that, if any record has to be neglected on account of the disparity of labour in relation to the duties involved, the choice should fall upon the one which is not often referred to? Sooner or later the fact is brought to light, and the trouble which ensues results in a temporary speeding up in this direction, with a slackening off in another.

The fact is that this record is a drag upon the efficiency of the department, and the solution of the trouble lies either in increasing the personnel, or in dispensing with (or considerably modifying) the record. Unfortunately, although it is known that certain duties are being neglected, no constructive action is taken by the management—nothing happens but a crude "speeding up," which shifts the trouble but does not eliminate it.

If it is decided that the progress department is the controlling factor, so far as routine is concerned, then it must be strong enough to control—if it is but a "follow up" or "chasing" department, it must still be thorough. If the centralized department causes delay by reason of being understaffed, and it is felt that no extra expense can be incurred, then economy and greater efficiency may be effected by decentralization. The writer has instances of greater effectiveness being achieved by a crude organization represented by two or three chasers than by a so-called modern centralized department, but he also has instances where the establishment of a recognized progress department has been followed by a tremendous increase in the factory output. It is all a question of the thoroughness with which the idea is applied.

Many industries outside engineering are applying the progress idea to manufacture, and with good results. The progress man is being recognized, and the progress department is a feature of the organization. Outside this country, too, the idea is being embraced, for in many factories on the Continent the organization is being developed "on English lines," which allows for the inclusion of a progress department. The merits of American and British methods of organization are being considered, and in most of the smaller factories the British methods gain the verdict, the reason being that they seem to cater better for the circumstance.

America claims pride of place in the matter of organization, yet outside her own borders her methods do not seem to flourish. Many attempts have been made to "Americanize" the factories of this country—our men have been sent to America to study their methods, and American organizers have come over here to teach us—yet the outcome so far is by no means striking. We are familiar with the British factory manager with a reputation based on twelve months' sojourn in "The States," but he does not seem to accomplish more than (and in many cases not so much as) the man who has never left his native heath. We have also seen the "real American," bubbling over with energy and vim, who continues to "bubble over" without any apparent effect.

This is not the fault of the individual, but rather of the conditions under which he labours. He has to organize and control hundreds (and maybe thousands) of people who have never been to America, and who consequently look at matters from a very different standpoint. It may be that, were the whole personnel "Americanized," it would be a comparatively simple matter to introduce American ideas of organization, in which case the factory manager with American experience would undoubtedly demonstrate his competency; but in default of this, it is hard to see how the manager's twelve months in the States will make him more effectual in the British factory, save only in the sense that the broader the experience the wider the outlook, which latter qualification is a business attribute of some worth.

But experience, to be of value, must be thorough and not superficial, and in this connection it may be remarked that the manager whose experience is limited to industrial concerns boasting an ultra-modern organization (whether British or American) is not likely to prove a conspicuous success when he endeavours to apply that experience to the control of a factory of more modest pretensions. Much better results are likely to be achieved in such a factory by the man whose experience has taught him not to expect too much, whose intimate knowledge of similar conditions elsewhere renders him appreciative and sympathetic. His methods may lack polish and appear crude in the eyes of the efficiency expert, but they have the virtue of being effective, and it is effectiveness that makes progress.

It is not denied that polish is an improvement when there is groundwork upon which it can be applied, and in this connection the educated man of business proves superior to his non-educated rival, always assuming that the educative process does not annihilate the business element. The head of one modern concern protested that he had "too many gentlemen" in his factory for the organization to be really effective; his factory officials were both educated *and* practical, but they lacked that directness which, allied to experience, not only enables men to control their fellows, but to stimulate them also. The "highly polished" individual (in possession of the necessary practical experience) may prove an ideal and an efficient works manager, provided that at least some of his subordinates are not so highly polished, and are as a consequence more capable of doing the "dirty work," or, as it might be more politely put, "performing the uncongenial tasks."

From this it may be gathered that the "progress idea" must be exploited by men whose "directness" is unquestioned, and who will not shrink from adopting the measures necessary to ensure success. This does not mean that the "bullying hustler" is recommended, for he is at the other extreme, and in efficiency he occupies a lowly position. What is wanted is a man of fair education, of quick perceptions and undoubted ability, whose outlook is broadened by experience; who is not only in the factory, but of the factory; a student of factory conditions and a keen judge of human nature.

In the opinion of the writer, progress work is at once one of the most interesting and one of the least understood of the phases of works organization, despite its constantly increasing popularity. It is looked up to in some factories and looked down on in others; yet it continues to thrive because its indispensability is recognized. There is no practical alternative, for the only thing put forward is planning, which itself can exist only when supplemented by an efficient progress organization, and this is made clear in the earlier part of this work.

In the preceding chapter a progress scheme is presented, designed to carry to its logical conclusion the work of the planner. In the succeeding chapters various phases of progress work are dealt with, and no matter how large or how small may be the factory—no matter the diversity of manufacture—the principles given can be applied, either in the form presented or modified to suit the requirement.

It was said in the first chapter of this book that a planning scheme can be applied to any factory, and too many people assume progress to be the antithesis to planning. As a matter of fact, no phase of the organization can exist without planning, and progress work is really a series of planning. The progress man who does not plan his course of action is not likely to meet with any measure of success, for haphazard "chasing" is an element of destruction rather than of construction—it is destructive to workshop efficiency because of its uncertainty and unreliability.

Progress work, carefully planned, co-ordinates the many and diverse factors in the factory organization, and it is not at all difficult to see, therefore, that in the non-repetition factory the planning of production is more often entrusted to a progress department rather than to a recognized planning department. In the circumstances it is difficult to plan, with any degree of accuracy, the sequence and form of the specific operation, as in the case of standardized manufacture, and it is felt by the management that the matter can be more expeditiously handled by the progress man, who, as the person responsible for satisfying the requirement, may be trusted to plan in accordance with his commitments.

There are many works managers, foremen and assistants who are keenly interested in progress work, but who are not satisfied that the best is being achieved by their own progress department. There are many progress men who are keen on their work, but who do not get a full measure of satisfaction from it. There are many young and enthusiastic individuals known as progress men and chasers, who are constantly "up against it," and have not the experience to keep them out of tight corners, or to get them out. There are also the young industrial students—the foremen and managers of the future—who are keenly alive to the value or organization as a whole, and of progress work in particular. To all these, as well as to the ordinary man in the shop (the worker, who has to work to orders and requires to know the meaning of these orders), the following chapters, setting out in detail the various phases of progress work, will probably be of interest, demonstrating as they do the value of the "progress idea" to industry.

CHAPTER VII

PROGRESSING SUPPLIES FOR A MACHINING DEPARTMENT

(a) From the Foundry, Smithy, and Press Shop

THE progress man attached to the machine shop is expected to see that adequate supplies of material are forthcoming, and to give prompt notice if there is any likelihood of delay. Supplies are drawn from a variety of sources, which may be classified as follows, viz.: (1) Material which, though considered as a raw product, still has to undergo an operation in at least one department before being ready for the attentions of the machinist. These include (a) iron, brass, and gun-metal castings, produced in the foundries; (b) forgings and drop forgings, produced in the smithy, and (c) light pressings, produced in the press shop. (2) Special material ordered direct from outside suppliers, which may include a wide range of goods, such as malleable iron castings, vulcanized material, and even partially machined metal parts. (3) Standard material held in stock, such as castings, steel, iron, brass, and copper bar and tubing, etc. (4) Partially machined parts from other departments.

The task of obtaining the materials shown under classification (1) will now be considered, and in dealing with it thus it is apparent that the departments enumerated, viz. iron and brass foundry, smithy, and press shop, are existent inside the factory. Were this not so, then such materials as are produced by these departments would of necessity be purchased from outside makers, and would be dealt with in precisely the same manner as the parts shown under classification (2), which forms the subject for the succeeding chapter.

The factory may be engaged upon a repetition line of manufacture, or it may be handling semi-standard work which can be adopted to the requirement of the customer, but in the main the method of obtaining supplies is the same. The standard castings, forgings, and pressings are produced to a weekly schedule, the figures being based upon the accepted factory output figures, whilst the isolated special parts required are given a definite delivery date.

Assuming that the output figure is 100 completed units per week, this means that 100 sets of details must be completed each week by the machine shop, and it also means that the foundries must produce 100 sets of castings, the smithy 100 sets of forgings, and the press shop 100 sets of pressings. If less than this number is produced by any one of the departments mentioned, then the factory output suffers, and although it is the duty of the officials of each department to ensure that the requisite production is maintained, it is the duty of the progress man in the machine shop to be closely in touch with the feeder departments, so that he may take action immediately it becomes apparent that a delay is likely to occur.

It is not enough for him to rely upon someone else. He may think that his duty lies in getting work through his own department, and argue that it is the business of the foundry, the smithy, and the press shop to furnish him with supplies. No doubt it is, but he must realize that, if he has not the necesary material, he is unable to complete his part of the bargain, and he is not a progress man if he is content to excuse himself on the score of shortage of material, making no effort to find out what the trouble really is.

He cannot, of course, instruct the officials of other departments, neither can he tell them how to perform their duties, but he knows when the material is due, and in his own interests he should institute inquiries. He may find out that the cause of the delay lies in his own department, as is instanced by the fact that in one case foundry work was delayed because the pattern plate was in the machine shop for a planning operation. Even though there is no evidence of delay, however, the closest co-operation should exist between the various departments, for the power of progress work lies in anticipating delay rather than minimizing it.

There must be no active interference, however, for this will do more harm than good. If the factory is properly organized, there is a progress organization in every manufacturing department, and all inquiries relative to delivery must be made through the officials of this organization. Many managers, however, whilst attaching a progress man to the machine shop, do not think it necessary to give like assistance to the feeder departments, and this point must therefore receive consideration.

In such a case the machine shop progress man must be in direct touch with the foreman of the feeder department, and it may be that, in certain cases, he is constrained to go somewhat farther than he should. We know that zeal is a very desirable characteristic, but this must be tempered by discretion, otherwise the result is contrary to expectation. In the first place, the foreman of a department cannot be expected to answer an inquiry at any minute of the day, and he is also averse to a never ending series of visits. The progress man naturally expects to get information, but there is no reason why at 10 o'clock, 12 o'clock, 2 o'clock, and 4 o'clock he should seek the same foreman in quest of information. One visit per day should be quite sufficient, and if the foreman is aware of the time of the visit, he is enabled to get together the particulars desired.

There is a tendency on the part of some foremen to shirk this responsibility, either by absenting themselves from their department at the time of the visit, or by professing themselves too busy for discussion. The progress man is not in a position to combat this resolution, and in many cases he seeks the information from a subordinate. This is quite in order so long as the foreman is prepared to accept responsibility for statements made on his behalf, and whilst matters are runnng smoothly he is content. It is when a statement is made, and the essence does not materialize, that the foreman professes his ignorance. A promise of delivery may be given, but it is not kept, and this fact is recorded by the progress man. An inquiry follows, and the foreman disclaims all knowledge of the affair, stating that the progress man had no right to accept as official the statements of a subordinate.

Unfortunately for the progress man, this is accepted by the management, for technically the foreman is right. It is obvious, therefore, that the progress man, whilst making use of the subordinate, must be circumspect in his dealings with him. If tact and ingenuity are displayed, many matters may be settled amicably without reference to the foreman, but when a really definite statement is required, which is likely to be referred to later, this must be made by the foreman, either in writing, or, if oral, confirmed in writing by the progress man.

In some factories the progress man from the machine shop is allowed a good deal of liberty in the foundry departments, for it is recognized that he can be of assistance. Whilst this is no doubt flattering, care must be taken to keep within bounds, for happenings may occur in which, through really no fault of his own, he is held culpable. It is nice to feel that one can walk unchallenged into the foundry, give advice, and generally accelerate production. One machine shop progress man was so zealous that each morning he visited the foundry, procured a shovel, and without let or hindrance dug the castings he required out of the sand where they were left for cooling, and conveyed them on the shovel (still hot) to the trimming department. So long as matters were well, this was winked at by the foundry officials, but when a casting was condemned as too hard to machine, the progress man was blamed for exceeding his duty, and the fault recorded against him.

Where there is no progress man attached to the foundries, smiths, and press shops, the machine shop progress man is expected to interest himself in patterns and dies. In the case of the foundry, and especially in regard to special castings, delivery cannot be effected because the patterns are not available, and the progress man, if he is keen upon securing the casting, will hasten to the pattern shop for the necessary information. He is probably not bound to do this, but he realizes that by so doing he is assisting in the right direction. After all, his business is to get the work through his own department, and he must of necessity agitate to get material into the department, but it is a very unproductive agitation which consists merely of giving reasons why he has been unable to meet his own delivery dates.

In the smithy and press shop, too, he must go "all out." These departments are dependent upon the tool room for the necessary punches and dies, and to the tool room he must go, if he would get satisfaction. He will not get a vote of thanks accorded him for his efforts, and if anything goes wrong he will probably be saddled with the blame; but on the other hand, if he sits tight and does no more than his bare duty he will not make much progress, and in the eyes of the management he will be regarded as a mediocre worker.

If he is ambitious and anxious for advancement, he will not object to hard work and a few risks, for anything which is worth having is worth striving for. It is not so much what people say, as what they think, which matters, and although harsh words may be the visible form of appreciation, the thing which matters is the appreciation (hidden, but still there) of the managers and the foremen, who speak of the progress man as a great nuisance, but think of him as a "smart young fellow, keen on his job, and ready to put himself out to do anything which may be necessary, even though he is not obliged to do so." And when you have gained *that* reputation you may consider that you are a little out of the ordinary, and that your feet are firmly planted upon the ladder of progress.

(b) From the Outside Supplier

In the repetition factory, the question of outside supplies is more a matter for the store than for the machine shop progress man, for, strictly speaking, there are no special parts, and therefore the whole of the necessary material should be in the store available upon demand. Sometimes, however, it happens that supplies are not always available, and then it is that direct communication may be resorted to, though only in given circumstances.

As the next chapter is concerned with obtaining supplies from the store, we may now assume that the material required is not available, even though it is a standard part which should be stocked. The progress man, upon receiving this information, is not content to let matters rest, and he wants to know when the material is expected. The storeman is unable to supply this information, and the progress man is referred to the store records section.

Now this section may be attached to the store, or, in some factories, to the progress organization, and the subsequent movements of the progress man are dictated by the system favoured. Assuming that the store, purchasing, and progress sections are separate organizations, a visit to the store records section may or may not give him the information desired. He can certainly learn the date of the placing of the requisition, and he may gain possession of the delivery date, but this section is not always in possession of the latest information. He must therefore journey to the purchasing office in order to acquire this, and he must convince the buyer that the material is overdue and urgently required, so that further steps may be taken to effect speedy delivery.

If the progress organization includes the store and purchasing departments, he may at once refer the matter to his own chief, who can instruct the buyer. This is the more simple proposition from the standpoint of the progress man, and is likely to be effective, for the progress chief, responsible for the feeding of all departments, and having the means at his disposal (in the control of buying), will personally interest himself in the matter. The main point, so far as the progress man is concerned, is to see that his chief is notified, and this notification may take the form of a "speed up" notice as illustrated. (See Fig. 26.)

SPEED UP OUTSIDE SUPPLIES

To PROGRESS CHIEF.   From............*J. Smith*............   Date........*9th Oct*........

To be Filled in by Progress Man					To be Filled in by Purchasing Clerk				
Works Order No.	Due for Delivery	Part No.	*Part Wanted* Description	Quantity	Purchasing Order No.	Date Ordered	Quantity Delivered	Promised	Remarks
17856	Oct. 18	477	Spring Washers	288	9371	Oct. 1	—	Oct. 12	
17859	„ 30	415	Brackets	50	9377	„ 4	10	10 per week from Oct. 8	
„	„	419	Thimbles	200	9379	„ 5	—	—	Wrote Suppliers Oct. 8th

FIG. 26

In the factory where the product is handled in batches comprising a comparatively small number, it may be that the material is specially ordered for each batch, very little being held in stock. In such a case the purchasing department must be closely in touch with the manufacturing departments, the progress man acting as the link. The buyer, of course, knows that a certain number of sets of material is required either weekly or monthly, as the case may be, but it often happens that certain items are overlooked, and a reminder from the progress man, in the form of a letter similar to Fig. 27, will be of great assistance.

The progress man should make sure that the material is not available before sending this notice to the buyer, although there are times when, through no fault of his own, he asks for material which is already in the factory. This statement will perhaps be regarded as a reflection upon the efficiency of the organization, but the infallible system has not yet been devised, and, good as the system may be, every little trouble cannot be anticipated. The human element, which the system is devised to assist, must control the system, and forms and papers are easily lost, the result being that when the memory is relied upon it sometimes plays one false.

The progress man must act upon information received, and if the storekeeper states he has not received certain material, he must be believed. So the item is included in the list sent to the purchasing department, and back it comes with a comment anent the

PURCHASING REMINDER

6th July.

To BUYING DEPARTMENT.   From PROGRESS DEPARTMENT.

K.V. PRODUCTION

As the first 100 chassis are to be completed this month, it is essential that all BOUGHT-OUT PARTS (rough and finished) are received without delay. The following is a list of the most important parts still outstanding, and special efforts should be made to secure the major portion of these this week. Will you please advise early what is being done, and the best promises of delivery you can get.

Part No.	Description	Remarks	Promise
359	Special Spring . .	Due yesterday	
333	Housing Nut	Completion should be	
334	Housing	specially urged	
360	Engine Support .		
371	Clutch Bracket .		
387	Bearing . . .	26 still required	
390	Worm Shaft . .	5 ,,	

FIG. 27

inefficiency of a certain department. The progress man, however, must not take this to heart, for he has gained his point. He could perhaps disarm criticism by making personal inquiries in the purchasing department, and not committing himself by writing, but the result would not be so satisfactory. Let us take a case.

An inquiry respecting certain material is made of the storekeeper, and this individual states that he has not seen it. The progress man then inquires of the buying clerk, and is informed that the material was received upon a certain date. Back to the storekeeper goes the progress man with the information, but the former is unable to trace any document dealing with the material in question, and again asserts that it has not been received. Another journey is necessary to the purchasing office, and the clerk is asked to furnish proof of delivery. He is not at all pleased and obeys with an ill grace, but the proof is forthcoming by the production of a receiving note, bearing the storekeeper's signature. After this, needless to say, the material is discovered.

It will be agreed that much time is wasted by this method, and it is certainly better for the reputed shortage to be reported in writing, for upon receipt of the list of the missing parts the purchasing clerk checks each item with his records, and if a certain item has been received, he states the fact and gives the date of delivery. This is done without the trouble of searching for proof, and the statement is accepted by the storekeeper more unreservedly than if it were made orally. It is only when he fails to locate the material that he demands proof of delivery, and although the written record may tend to implicate the progress man, he will at least get satisfaction with a minimum of trouble.

One buyer was fond of collecting these reports and sending them to the works manager, as proof of the inefficiency of the factory organization, but when challenged by the progress man he was unable to suggest a better alternative for dealing with the matter. As before explained, no system is perfect, although it must not be assumed that such cases as the one quoted are prevalent in a well-organized factory. As a matter of fact, such cases are rare, but the position may arise, and the progress man must know how it should be handled.

In the factory where special details are ordered from outside suppliers, the progress man may take up all cases direct with the purchasing department, as the parts covered do not usually go into stock, but are sent (after inspection) direct to the department concerned. The knowledge that the material is ordered outside is gained by a perusal of the specification list, which shows against each item the source of supply. The machine shop progress man in this case usually has a delivery date for the completion of all parts comprising the unit which are being handled by his department, and he must commence his inquiries concerning outside material early enough for this to be received, and the necessary operations completed by the date required.

From this it will be observed that the progress man must have a fairly good idea of the time necessary to get the material in, and also of the time necessary to complete the machining operations. In regard to the latter, the actual time allowance for each operation is known to him, but he has to take into consideration the claims of other work which has to be handled upon the same machine. He must, however, conduct his inquiries with skill, and not resort to panic measures. The man who is continually rushing to the purchasing department in a state of great excitement rarely commands confidence, and he is apt to be treated in a contemptuous manner. The buyer is impressed with the man who is ready to co-operate, whose word can be relied upon, and who gives an honest expression of opinion. "The matter is really urgent, and in order to meet my date I must have the material by so and so." It is a calm statement, and its honesty is unquestioned. "This part is late, and that part is late. This job and that job will be delayed, and I shall be obliged to revise my dates." This, delivered in a state of unsuppressed excitement, appears to the buyer to contain more than a coating of "hot air."

It does not pay to attempt bluff for it is so easily discovered, and the cry of "wolf" is disregarded, even when the wolf is actually there. If you *must* have the material by a certain date, say so, and stick to it, but if it is necessary for a point to be stretched, and it is possible for you to stretch it by a little ingenuity, then do so. The other fellow will appreciate it, and you will be the ultimate gainer.

So if you estimate that you should have the material on the 6th, and it is offered for the 10th, don't stand hard and fast for the 6th, if there is a possibility of the later date meeting the case. If you stick to the first date, the buyer may endeavour to meet you by purchasing elsewhere at a much higher figure, and if this is not absolutely necessary the progress man will have to answer to the management, and in addition, he will have forfeited the confidence of the buyer, which may have an adverse effect upon his future dealings with him.

In the matter of knowing the approximate time for the delivery of the material, this knowledge is gained by association and precedent. If the article is a malleable iron casting, it is absolutely useless to start inquiring, say, one week after the order has been placed. It is not often that a malleable casting can be delivered under three weeks, and the progress man must know this. In some cases there is a difference in the delivery times of similar materials, for whilst one supplier can deliver from stock, another must send to the manufacturers for the part. The supplier holding the part in stock probably charges a higher price, and the buyer, realizing that immediate delivery is not essential, places his order at the cheaper rate. The progress man commences his inquiries early enough to allow the buyer to take action—that is to say, he does not wait until the material is actually required before he makes a move.

When special material is received it must be inspected before being sent to the department, and the progress man must not endeavour to evade this. He is apt to chafe at what he considers unnecessary delay, especially if the material is somewhat behind in delivery, but he must remember that the inspector has a duty to perform. He can, if he uses tact, minimize the delay by stating the facts to the inspector, who will give the part priority over something received earlier, but which is not so urgently required.

He may be at fault himself in not notifying the inspector early enough, and the material may lie for a day or more without being inspected. It is of little use, then, trying to hustle the inspector, for most of the parts passing through his hands are urgently wanted, and he cannot be expected to know the exact degree of urgency of every part unless he receives due notification.

The progress man should arrange that he receives a daily list of all special material received, and either the buyer, or the head of the receiving section, will furnish this information upon request. With the list in his hands, the progress man can select the items which concern him, and compile a list of these in order of priority, sending this to the inspector. A form similar to Fig. 28 will be found quite satisfactory, and will obviate the necessity for personal visits.

With such a system, the question of delay in the inspecting section should not arise, for the inspector will see that the material, when passed, is at once sent to the department concerned. The progress man receives all delivery notes accompanying material into the department, so that operations may be commenced forthwith, and no delay may therefore be anticipated because of material arriving in the department without his knowledge. Delivery notes are very valuable documents to the progress man, and their uses are described in detail in another chapter.

(c) From the Works Stores

From a broad view point, it would seem a very simple proposition to get material from the store, for it is only necessary to ask for it and it is available. This is how it should be, of course; but, once again, practice upsets theory, and there are times when the machine shop progress man has to exercise his ingenuity in order to obviate delay.

When material is routed from the foundry, or the smithy or from an outside source, it is recognized as being a special case, and is treated accordingly. There are usually but a limited number

To INSPECTION DEPT.

From PROGRESS DEPT.   *Date*..........................

GOODS RECEIVED FROM OUTSIDE

WILL you please arrange for Inspection in the following order—

1 ....
2 ....
3 ....
4 ....
5 ....
6 ....
7 ....
8 ....

Please return this Form when completed.

(*Signed*)..

FIG. 28

of items so routed upon the specification list, and a special record can be made of these parts, which ostensibly call for the notice of the progress man. The other items (and these comprise a surprisingly large number) are routed from the store, and little notice is taken of these, it being assumed that material is available, and will be issued upon demand.

This assumption is not always justified, and delays often occur because the progress man takes too much for granted. It is obviously impossible for him to give the same attention to each of the 100 or more items which comprise the specification list, and so he concentrates upon the comparatively few items which are being specially handled to order in other departments. He has no reason to assume that one or more items listed from the store cannot be met, and as a consequence the deficiency in material is not discovered until it is actually wanted for machining.

The store man handling common bar material is no doubt dealing with scores of orders daily, and these, so far as possible, are executed in rotation, in the order received. He has a fair amount of material, but lengths are issued for this order and lengths for that, until at last it is apparent that there is not enough to go round. And, sure enough, it is the most important order which suffers.

The obvious retort is that if material has been supplied on one order, and there is not sufficient for another order more urgently required, there is no reason why the material should not be transferred from one order to the other. But, in the first place, what progress man will admit that an order is not urgent, until he has safely got hold of the material? The chances are that the order which could not be met is no more urgent than the other order, but it suits the progress man to pretend this, in order to impress the people responsible for supplies, and thus spur them on to greater efforts. Again, it is assumed that the material is not drawn from store until the operator is ready to start on the job, and if this is so, then it is impossible to divert it to another order, as it is already in use. The chances of transferring material already delivered are therefore remote, and when a shortage occurs the order immediately concerned necessarily suffers.

When this state of affairs exists, the progress man must be up and doing. It must not be inferred that nothing is done until he moves, for, thanks to efficient record keeping and to the scientific method of handling specification lists, the stores officials are already aware of their inability to meet all demands and have taken action.

The specification lists are posted as received, and although the material has not actually left the store, it has been appropriated so far as the records are concerned. For instance, the record card may show 2,000 lb. of 1 in. diameter bright drawn steel in stock, and the specification lists calling for the following quantities are received: (1) 750 lb., (2) 450 lb., (3) 1,000 lb. It will be seen from this that the last named cannot be cleared, and so an order for further supplies is placed on the purchasing department.

Now it may happen that the whole of the 2,000 lb. of material is in the store when the latest specification list is received, but it by no means follows that the material is sent out in the exact order as the lists are received. If there is a department sub-store it may happen so, but usually the material is left in store until it is actually required. The machining department has to take into consideration the delivery date of each order, and also the number of processes and the length of time required to handle these; it may be therefore that, in order to meet the delivery date, the material covered by the specification list last issued must be withdrawn first. As the storeman has 2,000 lb. of material, he can meet this demand and still have 1,000 lb. in reserve from which he can satisfy one of the remaining two orders.

It is here that the progress man must tread warily, for assuming that it is the first specification list which cannot be met, he may lay undue emphasis upon the date of the issue of this list, without taking into consideration the fact that the material has been utilized for a later order on his instructions. For it must be remembered that the store man issues material strictly in accordance with the demands presented by the shops, and if the demand for the material on No. 3 order is presented first, then that order is cleared.

The fact remains, however, that there is insufficient material in stock to clear the three orders mentioned, and it is essential that the progress man knows this as early as possible. Not that he can do much in the matter of speeding up, for material ordered to-day cannot, as a rule, be available in two or three days. We have shown that instructions to order further supplies were issued to the purchasing department by the stores record clerk immediately the deficiency was noted, and before the material was actually wanted, so it will be observed that no time has been lost.

In all probability the record clerk acquaints the buyer of the fact that an order cannot be met, and he may also give an approximate delivery date, based upon the urgency of the order in question. When this has been done a notification showing that the material is not available should be sent by the store record clerk to the machine shop progress man, similar to that illustrated by Fig. 29. If this procedure is followed, it will be seen that the work of the progress man is considerably lightened, and as he is aware of the deficiency before the material is actually required, he can at once take steps to obviate (or at least minimize) any delay which is likely to occur.

The store record clerk can easily supply this information, and with very little extra work, whilst it will obviate the necessity on the part of the progress man to worry through innumerable items routed from store in order to ascertain whether or not there is a deficiency of material. It will also eliminate a good deal of unnecessary work, for if it is known that the material is not available, the shop clerk will not trouble to write out a demand, the labourer will be saved a fruitless journey, and the storeman will not have to waste time explaining that the demand cannot be met.

To PROGRESS DEPT.

From WORKS STORE.
Date................*9th Oct*................

OUT OF STOCK

Order No.	Part No.	Description	On Stores Order
17856	477	Spring Washers	Purchasing
	490	Oil Elbows	5736
17857	471	Oil Strainer	5621

FIG 29.

The progress man, upon receipt of the notification, assumes that the purchasing department will do all possible to expedite delivery, and he knows that it is useless for him to "speed up" at this time. He is not, however, by any means idle, and he must adopt the course of action best calculated to obviate delay. It may be that the order affected is not particularly urgent, and he may be able to wait two or three weeks for the material. If this is the case, he duly notes the fact on his progress sheet, and in a week's time he commences to "speed up" the purchasing department, his activities becoming more aggressive as time goes on. If, on the other hand, the order affected is very urgently required the procedure adopted will be similar to the one described previously, viz. the requisition for material covered by the most urgent order will be at once presented to the store, other orders, received earlier but less important from a delivery standpoint, being held back temporarily to allow the most important order to have the first call upon what material is available.

When this is done, care must be taken to ensure that an accurate record of the transaction is kept. It will be noted that the stores records show the material appropriated to the orders as they are received: thus order Nos. 1 and 2 are shown as clear, whilst the shortage is shown on order No. 3. The notification issued by the store clerk shows that order No. 3 cannot be met, but as this is the most important order sufficient material is drawn from store to meet it, and so the shortage must happen in connection with one of the remaining two orders.

If reference is not made to this on the records, it is quite possible that trouble will arise at a later date, when the outstanding order of the three is to be handled. The progress man cannot remember all the details, and as he has cleared his most pressing order, it perhaps does not occur to him that another order will cause trouble later on. It may be that No. 3, being the most important, is cleared, and then follows No. 2. At last the material for No. 1 is required, but this is not available, and as the progress man has for the moment forgotten the circumstances, and he has, of course, no shortage note in connection with this order, he applies to the storekeeper for an explanation.

The store clerk reports that, so far as he is concerned, there is sufficient material in the store for that order, and then an interview with the store assistant reveals the fact that another order has received preference, and had first claim upon the material. The circumstances then are recalled by the progress man, but he has placed himself in a very invidious position, through not taking precautions to get his facts right. So, whenever it is decided to deal with the orders out of sequence, the fact should be recorded on the progress sheets dealing with the orders affected. If this is done, trouble and confusion at a later date are not likely to arise.

(d) From Other Manufacturing Departments

There are times when material must come into the recognized machine shop from one or more of the other manufacturing departments, and this must, of course, be looked after by the progress man. Sometimes the part in question is routed on the specification list from the department, in which case the progress man attached to that department must pay attention to the matter, but, on the other hand, the piece may be sent to the department because, in the opinion of the machine shop foreman or rate fixer, it possesses better facilities for handling a specific operation. A few examples may be cited.

It may be that in the factory there is what is known as a roughing department—that is to say, the part is roughed out to shape before being handled in the turning section. In this case the part is so routed on the specification list, and as the roughing department

Order No.....................F1732................   Sheet No................1........

SPECIFICATION

Quantity........4........   Type and Description........F.V. Double Gear Unit....

No. per Set	Drawing No.	Part No.	Name of Part	No. Required	Material	DEPARTMENTAL ROUTE				
						1	2	3	4	5
I	3121	I	Bracket .	4	CI	P	F	A	A	
I	,,	2	Cap . .	4	CI	P	F	A		
2	3137	4	Bevel Gear	8	Steel	O	A	G	A	A
2	,,	5	Pinions .	8	,,	S	A	G	A	A

FIG. 30

handles the piece prior to the machine shop, the progress man attached to the latter department simply shows upon his record that the material must come from the roughing department instead of from the stores.

In the case of an intermediate operation, it may be that all the gear-cutting machines of the factory form a section in a certain department, and whenever gear-cutting is required by the machine shop, the piece must be sent to this section for the operation. This is recognized by the people responsible for the issue of the specification list, and the gear-cutting section is shown thereon, as illustrated by Fig. 30. In this case, however, it will be observed that certain operations must be done in the machine shop before the piece can be sent for gear cutting, and so the progress man here has a double responsibility, for he must get the preliminary operations done, send the part to the gear-cutting section, and then press for its return, so that the later operations may be completed in accordance with the delivery date.

Another illustration is afforded by the piece which must be hardened before grinding. Several machining operations probably have to be performed before the piece is ready for hardening, and in connection with the latter process, it is very obvious that this cannot be rushed, and that adequate time must be allowed. It is up to the progress man then to get the first operations performed as expeditiously as possible, so that there will be no delay at a later date. As a rule, there is no progress man attached to the hardening shop, so the man attached to the machine shop must actively interest himself in the return of the part.

One other example may be cited under this heading, this dealing with the part upon which a fitting operation is necessary before the machining can be completed. In the case of a motor end shield, this has to be fitted with a cap before the boring operation can be handled, and both the end shield and the cap must undergo certain machining operations before they can be sent to the fitting shop for bolting together. Now, it is understood that these two pieces are not necessarily handled together in the machine shop— in fact, the opposite is the case, for the operations upon the two parts, save for the drilling, are quite different. In all probability they are not received simultaneously from the foundry, for they form different classes of work, and are handled by different moulders.

It is quite easy for the machine shop progress man to concentrate upon the end shield, and ignore the cap entirely. He rushes the end shield along, and gets it to the fitting shop, only to find, when he begins to press for delivery, that the work cannot be completed because the cap is not available. Then there is a hurried search for the missing detail, which in all probability is discovered in a raw state, and the end shield perforce must be delayed whilst the cap is being made ready.

This is no exceptional instance, for even the best of men make the mistake of concentrating upon the larger piece (which really cannot

be overlooked) and quite forgetting the smaller but equally important detail. Whilst it is important that both pieces should
receive equal attention, it may be said that it is not usually the
large piece which suffers through any lapse on the part of the progress man. It is big enough to be seen with ease—it is a definite
component part, and not an appendage thereof, and the various
foremen will see that it is not left behind. The smaller part (like
a cap) is treated with scant respect, and it is safe to say that if it is
overlooked by the progress man it will be overlooked by every one.
It is up to the progress man then, first of all, to give attention to
the cap, and when he is satisfied that it is making good progress,
he may then turn his attention to the end shield, which he will
find has made equally good progress so far, and this without his
assistance.

In each of the foregoing cases every department concerned is
shown upon the specification list, and the progress man attached
to the machine shop can see (1) the department from which the
piece must come, and (2) the department to which it must go. The
list shows the number of times the piece must be handled by his
own department, but it does not show the precise point at which
it must leave. In the main, the piece is received into the department as raw material, and leaves as a finished component, but
there are exceptions to this as the foregoing has shown.

It is expected that the progress man knows at what point the
piece leaves for another department, for this information may be
obtained from a perusal of the operations list issued by the rate
fixer. If the part, for example, has to go to another department
for gear cutting, after the turning and boring has been done, and
must be returned after gear cutting for the keywaying operation,
it will be found that the rate fixer has not issued orders for gear
cutting, as this operation is outside his jurisdiction. This point is
illustrated by Fig. 31, and if ordinary care is taken, the matter may
be handled without trouble.

We may now consider the cases which differ from the foregoing,
by reason of the fact that certain operations are handled by a
department not shown upon the specification list. In other words,
reference to the list will elicit the fact that the whole of the work
in connection with the piece is handled in the machine shop, and
yet, at the instigation of the foreman or the rate fixer, the piece is

actually sent to another department for the handling of at least one of the operations necessary.

All factories do not, of course, adopt the same methods, and it may be that in many the procedure about to be described is not favoured. In others, however, it is followed, and as the progress man may find himself in such a factory it is well to bring the point forward. As is well known, adaptability is one of the strongest assets of the progress man, for methods and systems differ so much that a man with a good reputation in one factory may easily come to grief when endeavouring to fathom the intricacies of the system favoured by another.

A DEPT.   Drawing and Part No.............3137/4........

OPERATION LIST

Name of Part.................Bevel Gear (steel).................

Operation No.	Operation	Machine No.	Time	Made for Orders
1	Turn . . .	15		F1732
2	Bore . . .	5		
3	Finish Turn . .	16		
4	Gear Cut . . .	G Dept.		
5	Keyway . . .	37		

FIG. 31

Our first illustration under this heading deals with "marking out" or "marking off," which is resorted to in connection with pieces where the quantity is too small to warrant the provision of jigs. In the factory engaged upon repetition work this is, of course, not necessary, but in the factory where the product is more or less special, "marking out" has to be considered. Sometimes the machine shop itself boasts of a "marking out" table, and when this is the case the progress man can handle the business without trouble, but the operation being more closely associated with fitting or tool making, it is usually handled by one of these departments.

Generally speaking, this operation precedes planning, shaping, slotting, and drilling, but unless the progress man knows which specific operation it precedes there is likely to be delay, for the piece is dumped down near to the "marking out" table, and is left to take its chance. As before mentioned, the "marking out" process is not shown upon the specification list, for it is wiser to leave this to the discretion of the machine shop foreman, seeing that it does not follow that the operations enumerated above must always be "marked out."

The issue of a delivery note in each instance would necessarily bring the movement of the piece to the notice of the progress man, but often the delivery note is not favoured in these circumstances—it being contended that too much clerical labour is involved for such a small process, whilst often the process could be completed before the delivery note reaches the progress man. It may be observed that the piece usually passes to the section responsible for the machining operation before it is decided to have it "marked out," for this decision is not arrived at until the drawing has been perused.

The better plan, then, is for the operator's work card to be sent direct to the progress man, this endorsed "to be marked out," and action could at once be taken. To put this more plainly, we will assume that a certain piece has passed the turning operation and has been sent to the milling section. The foreman of that section does not wait until he is ready to take the job in hand before he gives it a preliminary inspection, but as early as possible he will ascertain that he is in possession of the work card, drawing, fixing tackle, and the like. He will thus discover what sort of a job it is, and if he finds that it cannot be handled without first being "marked out," he sends the work card to the progress man in the manner described, at the same time sending the piece to the "marking-out table." This is a simple proposition, and if the section foreman does his part of the business there is little fear of delay.

The progress man can determine the relative urgency of each piece, for as a rule there is no shortage of work, so far as the "marking out" is concerned. The jobs which must be handled at once are speedily noticed, and are given attention, whilst those jobs which are not so urgently wanted are dealt with as the opportunity occurs.

One last illustration may be given, this dealing with a machining operation which is placed outside the department, at the instance of the foreman or the rate fixer. This is a case of special circumstances, for to all intents and purposes the operation can be handled by the department. It may be, however, that the tools or fixings which are necessary for this job are in another department, these being really designed for another purpose. The machine shop foreman, however, is aware of the existence of these tools, and as he has no wish to incur the expense of making another set for himself, he arranges with the foreman of the other department to handle the operation.

Or it may be that the piece to be operated upon is too heavy (or too large) for the machines. It may be thought that this should not arise, but in certain circumstances it does, as the following will show. The machining department is responsible for the machining

SUB-ORDER

Date ....

Works Order ....

FROM.. To..

Please do the following work—

....

....

To be completed by...

(Signed)..

Foreman.

Time and Materials to be booked against this Order Number.
This Form to be sent to Cost Office immediately job is completed.

FIG. 32

of, say, stator frames, and the department is equipped with the necessary machines for the purpose. But once in a way an order is received which covers a special type of frame, and when this is received from the foundry it is found to be much larger and much heavier than the recognized standard. The drilling machines, perhaps, can accommodate it with ease, but it may be that the table of the boring mill cannot hold it. As there is in the factory a machining department handling a heavier class of work, it is obvious that the machines here are more capable of dealing with the job in question, and the foreman must of course take advantage of this.

The method employed is for a sub-order to be issued upon the department asked to do the job, this giving the correct order number, and stating the operation to be performed, together with a date for completion. When the operation is completed, the sub-order is signed by the foreman of the department handling the operation, and it is then returned to the issuing department, and forwarded thence to the cost office.

The sub-order is illustrated by Fig. 32, and it is this document which enables the machine shop progress man to keep track of the job—to know when it leaves his department and the date upon which it is returned.

CHAPTER VIII

PROGRESS ROUTINE FOR SPECIFIC CIRCUMSTANCES

(a) A Specific Customer's Order

THE customer's order has individuality, and as such it must be handled. The order tells us that one unit (or more) is required for Messrs. Blank & Co., that the unit must be of a specific type and size, that it is required by the date mentioned, and that all costs in connection with manufacture of the said unit must be charged against the number at the head of the order.

We have to handle Blank & Co.'s order in conjunction with other customers' orders, and it may be that more than one order bears the name of Blank & Co. This, however, must not confuse the issue. We are not concerned with the whole range of orders emanating from Blank & Co. (at this point at all events) but we *are* concerned with order number 1,114, covering one type J, size 5 motor, for Messrs. Blank & Co., which must be delivered within four weeks from date. (See Fig. 33.)

MASTER ORDER

Date............*15th March*............... Order No............*1114*..............

Customer........*Messrs. Blank & Co*........

Delivery............*4 weeks*..............

MAKE AND SUPPLY

1 Type J, Size 5 Motor

Spec. 11196

(Signed)....................*J. Hurd*...................

Sales Manager.

FIG. 33

The moment this order is received in the progress office, it is under the control of the progress man responsible for the type of product covered, and he must never lose sight of the fact that the unit covered by that order must be completed and ready for dispatch within four weeks from the date received.

So far, the order has been received, and the fact duly recorded, and now the machinery must be set in motion to produce the article desired. To a certain extent, the factory system provides an automatic movement in regard to the issue of instructions, for at the same time as the progress man received his order a copy of this was received by the specification clerk, who thereupon commenced to draft out the detailed instructions in the form of specification sheets.

These bear the same number as the order, and give all particulars concerning the details which comprise the unit covered, showing the number of each detail required, the drawing number to which it is to be made, the material from which it is to be made, and the department (or departments) responsible for the making. Until this specification is received, manufacture cannot be commenced, and the first duty of the progress man, therefore, is to press for an early issue.

He must, of course, be guided by the delivery date, and the time necessary to get that specific type of unit through the manufacturing departments. He does not press for an immediate issue of the specification as a matter of course, for if he did that it is possible that this would be issued at the expense of an order infinitely more important as regards delivery. He must know the normal time necessary to complete manufacture, and he must be conversant with the present-day conditions in regard to the type of manufacture covered, and this knowledge guides him in the matter of speeding up instructions.

The order under review must be completed within four weeks, and this period may represent the normal time to be allowed for this specific type of unit. The manufacturing departments enjoying (at the present) normal conditions, no undue haste need be exhibited, and the specification clerk may be allowed ample time for the issue of the specification.

On the other hand, the shop conditions may not be normal, and the time allowance which in normal circumstances would be quite adequate, is now sufficiently "tight" to be regarded as a "cut date." This means the manufacturing departments having as much of those four weeks as is possible, and so pressure is applied with a view to getting the specification issued in the shortest time possible.

The specification having come to hand, the progress man is enabled to see what manufacturing departments are affected, and also the specific parts required for each. In the main, he knows in advance the departments interested, for there are certain departments definitely associated with that specific type of manufacture. For instance, all type J motors are assembled in a department (or at least a section) set apart for the purpose, whilst the winding is handled by a specific section of the general winding department.

There may, however, be special features involved, which bring other departments into the picture. The motor covered by our order may require a special pulley, which has to be cast in the foundry and machined in the machining department—the speciality may be a shaft, which has to be turned to given dimensions specially for this order, or special punched laminations may be required.

In each case an extra department has to be considered, and further, the effect of the speciality upon the progress of the product must also be considered. In the case of the pulley, this is not required until the unit is ready for erection, and this obviously does not affect the assembling and the winding of the core, which can be handled just as though no special feature were required. So long as the pulley is cast and machined by the time that the winding of the core is completed, that is all which matters, and the progress man can without difficulty issue the necessary delivery instructions.

A special shaft, or special laminations, however, require different treatment, for in either case the actual assembling and winding is held up until such time as the shaft or the laminations are ready. It follows, therefore, that these are the parts which must be concentrated upon, and if delivery dates are issued to the various departments, the departments responsible for the supply of these parts are given the shortest date.

Whilst the progress man is issuing the delivery instructions, the clerk in the rate-fixing office is making out the necessary work cards for the various pieces. The specification list shows the progress man the departments through which each piece must travel, but this list does not show what operations are necessary in each department. This information is obtained from the rate fixer, and is entered upon the progress sheet for future guidance.

Assuming now that all details are available for the core assembling, this operation receives early attention at the hands of the progress man, for he recognizes that when the core is ready for winding he may relax his vigilance, and turn his attention elsewhere. It may be that four or five days are required by the winding department for the winding of the core, and although the progress man keeps an eye upon it, and draws the attention of the foreman to it if it remains unattended for a day or so, he may now consider the parts required in connection with the final erection.

Assuming that a special pulley is required, it is now that he gives this his attention, and he will probably find that it has already been cast. If not, he must of course give attention to the foundry, and as soon as the casting is available he presses for the completion of the machining operations. At the same time, he satisfies himself that all other parts are available, whether these are supplied from the store or from another source. Everything must be in readiness against the arrival of the wound core, and when this comes to hand the work of erection can be commenced.

The urgency depends of course upon the nearness of the delivery date, for there is no point in hurrying the job if there is still plenty of time. If, however, delay has been experienced in the winding department or elsewhere, every effort must be made to minimize that delay. After the erection comes the test, and if the unit successfully passes this it is sent to the dispatch department, and order number 1,114 for Blank & Co. is marked "Completed."

(b) A " Long Operation " Job

The long operation job is the piece which has to undergo a great many processes, some of these processes occupying a considerable time, or, in other words, it is the piece upon which the greatest amount of time is spent, and it is what is known as the "limiting feature," so far as the delivery is concerned.

The progress man must know this piece before he can give a department a date for the completion of all parts covered by the order, otherwise he is liable to give a date which cannot be met. Date fixing must be intelligently handled, otherwise the prestige of the progress man will suffer, for nothing is more annoying to the shop officials than the receipt of instructions which are obviously impracticable.

Each item on the specification list must therefore be scanned, and it should not be difficult for the long operation job to be detected. Whilst the actual time necessary is not shown, it can be approximated, for a department delivery date does not exactly coincide with the actual operation time, seeing that shop conditions and the amount of other work already in the department must be taken into consideration. Still, it is obvious that the margin allowed for contingencies is not so pronounced in the case of the long operation job, as where the pieces are subjected to fewer processes, and this means that the long operation job must receive special attention at the hands of the department progress man.

To give a practical example, we will assume that a certain department is given one week in which to complete the whole of the parts covered by a specific order, and one of the pieces must undergo the following operations, viz.: (1) Turn, etc. (15 hours); (2) Mill (5 hours); (3) Mill (2 hours); (4) Drill (3 hours); (5) Shape (3 hours); (6) Drill (3 hours); (7) Slot (4 hours); Total 35 hours. This is the long operation job, the other pieces being limited to three operations of comparatively short length, and as the week comprises forty-seven hours, there would seem to be ample time for the handling of this piece.

But apart from the time necessary for the actual operations, there is the time for inspection and transit to be considered. In all probability the piece must be conveyed to the inspection department after each operation, and this means seven journeys and seven handlings by the inspector. Also, it is by no means certain that every operation will pass the inspector, and the possibility of the piece being returned to the operator for rectification must be taken into account.

There is other work, too, in the department, and it may not be possible to put this job in hand immediately upon receipt of instructions. So far as the initial operation is concerned, however, it is obvious that it must be taken in hand as early as possible, and the onus is upon the department progress man to see that there is no untoward delay here. In other words, a number of pieces are required for one order, and one or more of these pieces must undergo many operations. The progress man must give special attention to this piece (or pieces) with a view to ensuring its being completed by the date demanded.

Even though the first operation be taken in hand promptly, there is still danger of delay in connection with the succeeding operations, for the piece may arrive in a section at an inopportune moment. For instance, it may be that operations one and two are dealt with expeditiously, but when the piece comes up for operation number three, the machines upon which this operation must be performed may be occupied with very important work for a day or more. It needs some discrimination to determine exactly which job shall have precedence, for the slightest error of judgment may have serious consequences at a later date.

The matter must be constantly before the shop progress man, and to keep an accurate record of the movements he drafts out a

LONG OPERATION JOBS

Order No.	Drawing No.	Name of Part	Operations
2001	157	Lever . .	F. L. L. M. M. M. D. M. Sl. L.
,,	160	Bracket . .	F. B. L. L. M. D. Sl. D. D.
2006	181	Bevel Gear .	O. L. L. Gc. L. Sl. D. H. G.

FIG. 34

progress sheet for long operation jobs only, this being similar to Fig. 34. He does not wait for delivery notes to apprise him of a movement, for the rapidity of the movements precludes this, and personal investigation is necessary. This is a fine example of progress chasing, for manufacture and transit are being urged continuously, and the moment there is a stoppage the progress man wants to know why.

With a standard line of manufacture, the long operation job is just as important, for it is upon this that output is based. When it is determined that the output from the factory shall be 100 units per week, it means that 100 pieces of the longest operation job can be handled through all processes in a week, and it may be taken for granted that a liberal margin of time is not allowed. It follows, therefore, that constant watching is necessary, for if this piece fails then output suffers as a consequence.

It is probable that, of the 200 or more component parts comprising an assembled unit, not more than three or four need really be termed "long operation jobs," for these three or four are of such magnitude that others, though necessitating quite an amount of time for handling, are nevertheless small in comparison. The body of an 18-pounder shell, for instance, is subjected to at least twenty different operations; the connecting rod for an aero engine often undergoes fifteen operations, and the automobile crankshaft, with at least a dozen operations, are just a few instances of what constitute long operation jobs.

The illustration (Fig. 35) shows a chart which was designed for recording the movements of a long operation job, and this was used with good results in a large armament factory. This chart was readjusted every few hours, and by this means any "lagging behind" was speedily apparent.

It is sometimes the practice for one progress chaser to devote his time exclusively to long operation jobs, whilst another interests himself in the smaller components. This, of course, ensures adequate attention being given to the one without the other suffering from neglect, for it may be observed that delays may be occasioned owing to the smaller pieces being overlooked. As mentioned elsewhere, the foremen and chargehands usually take note of a large piece, and frequently miss the smaller ones, but with so much at stake the larger pieces must not be left entirely to the foremen who, even though they may show commendable promptitude in putting it into process, evince no interest in its movements when the operation with which they are concerned is completed.

Another point is that the pieces must be handled in correct sequence, otherwise trouble is likely to ensue. If the part in question is of large dimensions, it bears a distinctive number, and it is the movements of this one part which matters. It is important to know just how long one given part lies in any one section, and also to know whether or not the inspector has held it back for any reason. It may be that the piece numbered 21 has been handled up to operation six, and then there is a stoppage. Shortly afterwards the piece numbered 22 arrives at this stage, and is then passed

CARRIAGES

OPERATIONS	W.O. 1897 QUANTITY 15 DELIVERY 21/10	W.O. 2001 QUANTITY 10 DELIVERY 31/10	W.O. 2013 QUANTITY 20 DELIVERY 10/11	W.O. 2116 QUANTITY 16 DELIVERY 27/11
1 FORGING				
2 LINE OUT				
3 TURN FLANGE				
4 TURN BASE				
5 MILL SIDES				
6 MILL TOP				
7 BORE				
8 FIT BRACKET				
9 RIVET BRACKET				
10 MACHINE ALL FACES				
11 SLOT				
12 DRILL				

Fig. 35

through for the next operation. The chart must show that the latter number has advanced farther than the former, for then it will be seen that something is amiss, and inquiries will be made. If No. 21 takes the position really held by No. 22, and then others follow in succession, it will be some time before it is apparent that something is wrong with No. 21, and then in all probability there will be some difficulty in locating it and getting to the root of the trouble.

(c) A Stock Assembly

Let us assume that the progress man is responsible for the completion of a given number of small assemblies each week; that is to say, he must ensure all details being in the assembling shop early enough to permit of the number being completed in accordance with the schedule. We will take for the purposes of illustration the factory interested in the manufacture of hand-operated lifting gears, and it may be remarked here that these are made in a number of sizes and types, so that there is no lack of variety.

It will also be assumed that a great many of the details are to a common design; that is to say, the detail made to a specific drawing may be used in connection with several different assemblies. Whilst this undoubtedly simplifies manufacture, it has the effect of placing additional responsibilities upon the shoulders of the progress man, for he must appropriate the common stock in a manner calculated to satisfy the requirements of each class of assembly.

In the first place, the progress man receives a list (see Fig. 36) each Monday morning, this showing the state of the stocks up to the previous Saturday, and it is the business of the progress man to bring these stocks to at least above the recognized minimum figure by the following Saturday. He must also bear in mind that during the week a number of sales will be effected, and although these cannot of course be pre-determined, the fact that a further call upon the stocks will be made must be taken into account. On the other hand, it is decreed that the recognized figure must not be exceeded, and in allowing for contingencies the progress man must beware lest he transgresses this rule.

This is a fairly stiff problem for the progress man, but the position is made easier when he carefully considers the different lists and calculates from them what weekly sales have been effected previously. It is not difficult for him to do this, if he marks his list up accurately and keeps a copy, for he will have before him the stocks of the previous week; the number he put into stock during the week; whilst the next list will show the state of the stocks after he has replenished them. By this he can see what sales have been effected, and whilst the sales of course vary from week to week, he will be able to strike an average, and make provision which, whilst not causing the maximum figure to be exceeded, will ensure the stocks being shown at a figure beyond the minimum.

TYPE P UNITS IN STOCK

Date................*20/10/*................

In Stock last Week		Sold during Week	Received during Week	Now in Stock	Stocks Allowed		Minimum to be Completed this Week
					Max.	Min.	
A	103	20	—	83	150	50	70
B	283	116	100	277	300	100	23
C	171	106	190	255	300	100	45
D	70	10	—	60	75	25	15
E	75	—	—	75	75	25	—
F	100	30	—	70	150	50	80

FIG. 36

Theoretically there are adequate stocks of component parts available, and assembling is the only process to be considered, but in practice this is not always the case. It is quite possible that a good number of component parts are available, but much depends upon the particular classes of apparatus acquired and the parts necessary for these. As an example, let us assume that one certain part is associated with three different sizes of one class, and two different sizes of another, one being required for each specific assembly. Now, in one week the stock requirements are as follows, viz.: First class, 50 size 1, 100 size 2, and 100 size 3, whilst the second-class requirements are 25 size 1, and 10 size 2.

This means that 285 parts are required, and probably not more than 200 pieces are available. This latter figure is in all probability considered a fairly large stock, but it is not sufficient for the requirement, and the progress man must endeavour to supplement it by hustling further supplies through the machining departments. He may be successful in getting the required number, in which case all is well, but on the other hand, his efforts in this direction may not be crowned with success.

When this is the case (and it is more often so than not) he is faced with the task of appropriating the 200 pieces to the best advantage, and this can only be accomplished by a thorough understanding of the different requirements, and what the figures given upon the list really portray. It is, of course, clear that 285 pieces are required for the purpose of completing that number of assemblies, but as the number is out of the question, it is obvious that something must be dropped. But what?

A careful perusal of the stock requirements list will no doubt elicit the fact that in at least one instance the class of apparatus covered is a somewhat slow-moving line, and that, although the number in stock this week has fallen below the minimum figure, that number is still sufficient for a week or more, judging by previous sales. It may be that each sale effected comprises but a single unit, and that not more than three or four are sold during any one week. As the minimum figure is 10, and there are actually nine at the moment in stock, it seems fairly safe to hold back manufacture for one week and thus allow the parts to be used in connection with an assembly which is more likely to be in demand.

On the other hand, it may be that this assembly has already been neglected, and that it is absolutely necessary for stocks to be replenished. If this is so, then one of the other assemblies must be considered, with a view to at least reducing the quantity aimed at. It may be well to state here that the class of apparatus in popular demand is obviously manufactured in large numbers, for heavy stocks are held against demand, and the minimum figure is fairly high. Where the demand is not so insistent, the stocks are small, and the minimum figure is, of course, proportionately small.

We may assume, therefore, that the units falling into what has been called first class are of the popular variety, because of the larger requirements, whilst those labelled second class are not so much in demand. As it has been decided that the second class requirements in the instance under review must be met, it is necessary to see how reductions can be made in regard to the first class to make this possible, and yet at the same time to ensure a sufficiency of stocks of the first class units.

We note that the requirement for size 2 is 100, but it does not mean that this number is necessary for the stocks to reach the minimum figure. In all probability the minimum figure in this case is 90, and the maximum 180, the minimum being based upon three weeks' and the maximum upon six weeks' sales. The actual stock at the moment is 80, and it is necessary to manufacture a further 100 to ensure adequate supplies. When there is a shortage

To................*Mr. Smith*................

FITTING DEPARTMENT
Date................*22nd Oct*................

All details are available for the Units given below.

Type	Class	Batch No.	Quan.	Parts Drawn from Store	Units Completed
P	A	416	50	22/10	10 26/10 10 27/10
,,	B	418	40	24/10	20 27/10
,,	C	420	50	24/10	
,,	F	421	100		
Q	A	423	100	25/10	
,,	C	424	30		
,,	D	425	50		

FIG. 37

of component parts, however, it may be considered desirable to manufacture but 50 units during the week, and so release 50 component parts for other and more important purposes.

The allocation of the 200 pieces available then may be as follows: First-class manufactures, size No. 1 (50), size No. 2 (50), size No. 3 (70). Second-class manufactures, size No. 1 (20), size No. 2 (10). Total 200. This allocation would ensure supplies of each unit, and as further parts are being urged through the shops, it is quite possible that early the following week further units may be assembled. The fitting shop foreman is supplied with a list similar to Fig. 37, showing the assemblies for which component parts are available, this being adjusted daily as further parts come to hand.

(d) " Rush" Orders

It may be thought that the "rush order" has no place in the well-organized factory, but as a matter of fact it is very real, and must be catered for. Sometimes the "rush" is due to factory troubles in the earlier stages; at others it is due to failure to supply the unit from stock, whilst again, in order to secure business, the firm deliberately gives a "cut" date for delivery.

When the latter is the case, a definite procedure is adopted. The requirement must be fairly standard, or there must be special parts well advanced in connection with a long-dated order which can be utilized. For the purposes of illustration, we will in each instance assume that the order covers a 20 h.p. induction motor.

We will assume that the scheduled delivery for this type and size of motor is four weeks from the date of order, of which one week is required for the preparing and issuing of instructions to the shops. In certain cases, however, when delivery is of vital importance, and the only speciality in connection with the product is the winding, it is possible to guarantee delivery within ten days from receipt of order, this being virtually delivery from stock.

It is obvious that only a low percentage of orders can be dealt with in this manner, and that special measures are necessary to guard against delay. Such an order must receive preferential treatment at all stages, and yet this must not have the effect of extending the delivery dates of other orders on hand. In other words, although the details comprising this order must have priority over those comprising the other orders on hand, the latter must not be held back long enough to affect the delivery date.

This calls for some ingenuity on the part of the progress man, for he still has his commitments to meet, despite the special effort he is called upon to make in connection with the "rush" order. It is an easy matter to rush through the details comprising one order if the claims of all other orders can be disregarded for the time being, but this is not permissible. Let us see what happens.

In the first place, it is obvious that one week cannot be spared for the issue of instructions, and these must be in the shops within three days. As all parts are standard with the exception of the windings, specification lists already compiled are kept in reserve, and immediately an order is received the winding specification is added and the list issued to the shops without delay. All instructions are indorsed "Urgent Delivery," so that every one concerned is enabled to recognize the necessity for prompt action.

Upon receipt of the instruction in the store, the details are at once issued, these bearing a brightly coloured tally. The stator and rotor cores are assembled, and these, bearing a similar tally, are sent to the winding department. It may be observed that each department head is advised by the progress department of the receipt of a "rush" order, so that everything possible is done to ensure the prompt handling of any part. For instance, the coils are wound and awaiting the receipt of the stator and rotor into winding, so that they can be taken in hand immediately. The foreman or chargehand makes arrangements in advance so that the necessary labour is available, and this without causing any dislocation in the department.

Whilst the winding of the stator and rotor is proceeding, the details required in connection with the final fitting are collected together, and upon the arrival of the parts from the winding department the final fitting is put in hand, and in due course the unit is passed to test, and thence to the dispatch department, the distinctive tally not being removed until the unit is ready for packing.

In this case all the necessary parts are carried in stock, so that there is no question of any special machining. Care must, of course, be taken to ensure there being sufficient parts in stock to meet the demand, otherwise the chances of meeting a cut delivery date are somewhat remote.

Sometimes, however, the firm is anxious to secure an order which is not altogether standard, and the decision usually rests with the head progress man. He is advised of the special features and must decide whether or not the required delivery date can be met. It may be that a somewhat similar unit is in hand in connection with another order, and as certain of the details are well advanced it is possible to transfer these to the new order, and hustle through replacements at all speed.

Again, assuming the unit to be a 20 h.p. induction motor, the special features in this instance may be the windings, endshields, and bearings. For the windings, however, punched laminations which are not standard are required. It is ascertained that similar laminations have been used before, therefore the punch and die are in existence. It is quite possible, indeed, for such laminations to be actually made for another order, and further investigation shows that this is so, and that they are just being assembled in a frame. As the frame is standard in each instance the parts are commandeered for the new order, and an urgent order is placed upon the press shop for replacements. The frame when assembled is sent for winding, and the rotor is dealt with in like manner. Attention is then turned to the endshields and bearings, and as it is found that those for use in connection with the older order have been cast and are in process of machining, they are transferred to the new order and hustled through with all speed. At the same time an urgent order is placed upon the foundry, so that replacements may be furnished at the earliest possible moment.

This procedure may be varied, but in any case the progress man has two rush orders to contend with, for whilst priority must be given to the first, the second, too, must receive adequate attention. It is obvious that cases of this description must be rare, otherwise the whole organization would speedily become dislocated, but from time to time the progress man is called upon to extend himself, and he must rise to the occasion.

Sometimes, owing to a factory trouble or other cause, a rush is necessary in connection with one specific detail. It may be that the part has been scrapped when fairly well advanced, and the replacement must receive special attention in order to obviate delay in assembly, if this be at all possible. To cope with this emergency, a special work card may be issued in place of the ordinary type, this card being quite distinctive, and bearing the word "Lightning," accompanied by what purport to be flashes upon the back.

This card can be issued only by a high authority, and is not used as a "speed up" owing to negligence on the part of a progress man. The latter must needs have a good case before approaching the head for the purpose of soliciting the issue of a "Lightning" card, and as a consequence it is treated with respect. The card accompanies the detail upon its travels, and is the authority for the part having absolute precedence. There must be no wait—if the machine upon which the operation must be performed is engaged upon other work, that work must be stopped at once, even though this involves the pulling down and resetting of the machine. As may be imagined, this is apt to be an expensive procedure, and is not to be put into motion lightly. It is only in a case of real emergency, when the consequences of delay are particularly serious, that the chief sanctions the issue of a "Lightning" card.

(e) Suspensions, Releases, and Cancellations

Sometimes in the course of manufacture the instruction is received to "hold-up" or "suspend" work, this applying either to the whole order, or to specific items covered by the order. As a rule, the official "hold-up" notice is issued to the progress department from the drawing office, and it must be promptly acted upon. It does not often appear in connection with standard lines of manufacture, but is usually associated with the product which is being manufactured to the customer's requirement, and may be occasioned by a change of desire on the part of the customer, or on account of a change in design which has suggested itself to the firm's engineers.

It may be that the customer wishes cancellation, or the substitution of a different type or size of unit, but as nothing definite is decided upon at the moment, a "hold-up" notice is issued for the suspension of all work covered by the order, and it is for the progress man to see that this is obeyed promptly. Instructions are passed on to each and every chargehand and section leader interested in the order, and the progress sheet is endorsed accordingly.

When the "hold-up" covers specific items, only work on these is suspended, the remaining details being progressed through as heretofore. Unless the "hold up" is subsequently cancelled there will, of course, come a time when the whole order is in abeyance, for obviously the work cannot be completed until the items covered by the "hold-up" are released. It is understood, however, that the "hold-up" remains in force until it is officially cancelled by either a "release" or a "cancellation" notice.

A "cancellation" notice may be issued without a preliminary "hold-up," this, of course, when matters are definitely settled and it is known that the work is not required. In some instances the "cancellation" notice covering the whole order is not issued until the state of the product has been ascertained by reference to the

Lightning

Order No.	Drawing No.	Quantity	Description	All Work must be Completed by

NO DELAY

MUST ON ANY ACCOUNT OCCUR WITH THIS ORDER

(*Signed*)..

FIG. 38 (*Front*)

All Time, from the Issue of this Card to the Completion of the Job, must be accounted for.

CARD ISSUED

Time.................................. Date...

Received by		Time	Date	Operation	Finished at		Remarks
Name	No.				Time	Date	

This Card must accompany the Job at every stage, and must be signed by every person (Foreman, Operator, Inspector, or Labourer) handling any work in connection with the Job covered.

FIG. 38 (*Back*)

progress department, for if work is well advanced, and a number of special features are involved, the firm may refuse to accept cancellation. This illustrates the importance of the progress records being quite up to date, so that accurate information is available.

When cancellation of the whole order has been accepted, the notice is promptly obeyed. The "hold up" (if one has been issued) is automatically superseded by the "cancellation" notice, operation cards and orders are withdrawn and cancelled, and the details already manufactured are sent to the store. So far as partly finished parts are concerned, a list of these may be forwarded to the

HOLD-UP

Date..

To DEPTS..   Spec. List No................................

No further work is to be done in connection with................................

....

until this Notice is withdrawn.

(Signed)..

FIG. 39

drawing office, and it is for the draughtsman or the engineer to determine whether these shall be completed, whether scrapped, or held in stock in their present state.

The cancellation of specific details happens at times. The original specification may have included a pulley, but later this is superseded by a coupling, thus the item showing the pulley is cancelled, and a new item showing the coupling is added. In another case the shaft may be held up and subsequently cancelled. Now it is obvious that a shaft is required, but this is to a new drawing, and is covered by a new item added to the specification list. If the original drawing of the shaft is altered to suit the new design, then no additional item appears upon the specification list, and the original item covering the shaft cannot therefore be cancelled. In this case a "release" notice is issued, in the form shown on the next page.

A "release" notice is the instruction to "go ahead," and this must be received before any work held up can be proceeded with. The change of design, if any there be, is not necessarily specified upon the notice, although it sometimes appears thereon as a precautionary measure. The issue of a "release" notice simply means that the work may be resumed, and assuming that alterations to the dimensions given upon the drawings have been made in the meantime, work must necessarily proceed in accordance with the alteration.

As an example, the part held up may be the shaft, the suspension of work being for the purpose of making an alteration to the drawing. One dimension only is altered, say, from $2\frac{1}{2}$ in. to $2\frac{17}{32}$ in., and as the drawing number remains as before there is no necessity for the item upon the specification list to be cancelled—so a "release" notice is issued.

RELEASE

Date..............................

To DEPTS..   *Spec. List No*..

Work can now proceed in connection with............................

....

This supersedes Hold-up dated..

(Signed)..

FIG. 40

It is understood that the hold-up, cancellation, and release notices, when these do not cover the whole order, refer to specific *items*, and not directly to *details*. It is obvious, of course, that it is the detail which is really concerned, and that it is only incidentally that a certain item is associated with the detail in question. The reference to the item rather than to the detail, however, prevents a good deal of confusion in connection with the issue of these notices, and a definite procedure can be adopted without fear of misunderstanding.

Thus the "hold-up" refers to item 85, and item 85 is the shaft. When that hold-up is superseded by a "release" notice, no change is made in regard to that item, and work proceeds in accordance with the original instruction. If, however, the hold-up is superseded by a "cancellation" notice that item ceases to exist, and obviously the part covered by that item (the shaft) disappears.

But with the receipt of the "cancellation" notice (or maybe prior to receipt), item, say, 150 is added to the specification list, and this item covers a shaft. As this item has never been held up, no release notice is necessary, and work in connection with it may proceed forthwith.

Whilst work may proceed in connection with the addition even whilst the original shaft is still "held up," it is wise for the progress man to point out to the draughtsman that the first item has not been officially cancelled, as this may have been overlooked. This is particularly so when, for example, a pulley is superseded by a

CANCELLATION

Date..

To DEPTS............................   *Spec. List No*...

The following is now cancelled.

....

This supersedes Hold-up dated..

(*Delete if no Hold-up has been issued.*)

....

FIG. 41

coupling, as it is not definitely known by the progress man whether the coupling is to displace the pulley, or whether it is an additional detail. He may assume (and that correctly) that the former is the case, but definite knowledge, and not assumption, is necessary, and the order should not be closed until an official intimation is received that the pulley is not required.

Each notice should clearly demonstrate its mission, and the words "hold-up," "release," or "cancel" should be boldly displayed, whilst different coloured paper should be used for each. For example, the "hold-up" notice may be printed upon yellow paper, the "release" notice upon blue, and the "cancellation" notice upon red, so that confusion is impossible. If the whole order is affected, then "all work" should be typed upon the notice, whilst if but a portion of the order is affected, the notice should state "item No. —" or "items — to —."

The progress man must see that all alterations are shown upon his copy of the specification list, and also upon his progress sheet, whilst if the alteration is calculated to affect the completion date, he must at once notify the sales office or whichever department is concerned. He must take the initiative in this connection and not wait for a lead, for he knows better than any one what effect the alteration will have upon the delivery date. The sales office, naturally enough, does not wish to extend the date, and will take no action unless an intimation is received from the progress department that the original date cannot stand. Such intimation must, however, be advanced at the earliest possible moment, otherwise the sales office assumes that no extension of the delivery date is necessary.

(f) Working to Sales Office Requirements

In some factories engaged in the production of one specific type of apparatus the requirements of the sales department are met from stock. The warehouse (or dispatch) clerk holds a record of completed units in stock, and when the figure reaches a certain point a notification is put through to the works, with a view to urging further supplies. By this means production is regulated in accordance with actual sales requirements, and whilst on the one hand excessive stocks are avoided, on the other the works are enabled to maintain production so that "delivery from stock" can be the answer to every inquiry.

It is recognized that this is a very simple method and limited in its scope, but under the conditions mentioned earlier it is quite efficient, and is to be preferred to more elaborate systems. There are other factories however, which, although concerned with but one type of apparatus, cannot be content with this record, the reason being that the volume of sales orders is too large to permit a surplus stock of completed units from which new orders can be met. Apart from this the product is of somewhat substantial dimensions, and in its completed state represents a large sum of money—the management, therefore, whilst appreciating the importance of speedy delivery, is nevertheless constrained to adopt a cautious policy, by permitting sales to lead manufacture.

But, whatever may be the controlling factor, there are factories where "delivery from stock" in its literal sense is impossible, and the "quick delivery" feature—one week, two weeks, and so on— is exploited. This means that manufacture in the main must always be well advanced, and it means also that the works must be cognizant of the sales office requirements in order that there may be no undue delay in the execution of any order. It is not expected that the works shall deal with each specific sales order strictly upon its merits (from the standpoint of delivery), for the allocation of each completed unit can be made by the dispatch clerk (acting upon sales office instructions), but the works must know the extent of the sales office commitments, so that the maximum effort is made each week to discharge them.

It is obvious that a system must be devised with this end in view, but it need not be elaborate in order to be effective, especially if the weekly production of completed units is comparatively small (in number). Two methods are cited, therefore, for the purposes of illustration, and both may be recommended to the manager of the small factory who is desirous of installing an inexpensive yet effective medium through which the requirements of the sales office may be ascertained and catered for.

The first method illustrated is perhaps the most elaborate of the two, but it is simple to handle nevertheless. The chart (see Fig. 42) is of the combination variety, and shows not only the actual sales requirement, but also how far this requirement is met at any time by the number of units completed, and, in addition, the prospects for the future as shown by the amount of detail completed. The chart, which is drafted on squared paper, shows in the first instance the actual sales requirement, and, immediately beneath this, the number of units completed. Then appears a list of the whole of the details comprising the unit, and, assuming that at a certain date the sales requirement stands at 30, and the units completed at 20, a glance at the detail portion of the chart will show precisely which component parts must be speeded up to permit the completion of the ten units outstanding against the sales requirement.

The method of acquainting the works of the sales requirement may be as follows: Each day a list is received in the progress department from the sales office, giving brief particulars of all new orders received, and the progress clerk, upon receipt of this, blocks out the number of squares on the chart corresponding to the number of units covered by the list. Assuming that a new chart is about to be operated upon, and that the first list received covers five units, the clerk would block out the first square on the top line, then the

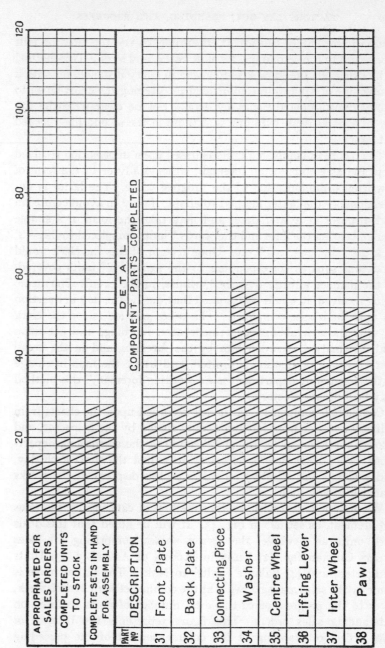

Fig. 42

square immediately beneath it, returning to the top line for unit
No. 3, and to the second line for unit No. 4, and so on. This method
of blocking out the squares is followed in every instance, for with a
double line of squares (recommended for keeping the chart down to
handy dimensions) the message would not be clear were the top
line of squares dealt with first and those in the second line blocked
out later.

The record of completed units is based upon information received
from the assembling shop foreman, either orally or in the form of
a written communication to the progress office. The latter is un-
questionably the better method to adopt, if only to avoid confusion
and disputes at a later date, and may take the form of a simple
memo, bearing the date and the words "units completed to-day—4,
Nos. 201, 202, 203, 204," etc. Upon receipt of this the clerk would
block out squares corresponding to the number of units covered,
in the manner already described, whilst, in the event of no memo
being received, it would be assumed that during the day in question
no units had been completed. The other method is for the clerk
to visit the assembling department each morning, and act upon
oral information accorded him by the foreman, and in the small
factory where production is limited, and where the man in charge
of the assembling department is a "working foreman," this method
may be quite satisfactory.

Completed component parts are recorded upon the charts from
delivery notes or from job cards, duly signed by the inspector, and
also by the foreman (or the storekeeper) in the assembling department. Very little time is necessary to adjust the chart each day,
and a simple yet effective record is at the disposal of the works
manager at any time.

We may now deal with another method of catering for the sales
requirement, as set out in Fig. 43. It will be noted that this deals
with units as a whole, the figures shown comprising (1) Sales
Orders Outstanding, (2) Units in Process of Assembly, (3) Units
Completed, and (4) Balance (units) to Make. The initial move is
made by the sales manager, who, at the commencement of each week,
gives to the progress office the total number of units required on
outstanding sales orders. This figure represents the balance of
sales orders outstanding at the commencement of the preceding
week, minus the number of units completed by the works during

that week, plus the units covered by new sales orders received during the week. In other words, if, at the commencement of week ending 30th June, the balance outstanding on sales orders = 36, the number of units completed by the works during the week = 10, and the units covered by new sales orders received = 4, the balance of sales orders outstanding at the commencement of week ending 7th July = 30, the figure selected for commencing the table illustrated.

PRODUCTION TABLE

Week Commencing	Sales Orders Outstanding	Units in Process of Assembling	Units Completed	Balance to Make	Remarks
July 7	30	15 15 — 30	10	~~15~~	
July 14	50	20 15 — 35	15	~~30~~ 15	
July 21	40	20 10 — 30	23	~~20~~ 10	
July 28	61	7 10 15 — 32	23	~~54~~ ~~44~~ 29	
Aug. 4	56	9	47		

FIG. 43

This figure is entered upon the table by the progress clerk, whose next business is to record what is being done to meet the requirement. It is not expected that, because the balance outstanding on sales orders = 30, a corresponding number of units are at once put in hand for assembling, for it is unlikely that there is a sufficient volume of detail available, or that the assembling department can cope with such a high rate of production. On the other hand, it is not usually the case that all sets of detail put in hand for assembling during one week are completed by the end of that week, and it is reasonable to assume that, toward the end of the week, one batch of details is put in hand for assembling, with a view to commencing the shops' campaign against the sales requirement of the succeeding week.

The progress clerk, then, must ascertain how many units are in process of assembling, and enter this figure in the appropriate column —having done this, he can immediately enter, under the heading of "Balance to Make," the required figure. A glance at the table will show that, for week commencing 7th July, the sales orders outstanding = 30; units in process of assembling = 15, and the balance to make = 15.

This is all that appears at the commencement, but during the week progress is made, and this is recorded accordingly. Thus, it will be seen that the "Balance to Make" (15) has been put into process, and the figure transferred to the appropriate column; also, that during the week, ten units have been completed, a record being made of this. At the end of the week the necessary totals are made, which give the comparisons and also form the basis of the succeeding week's record.

At the commencement of the following week a new notification is received from the sales office, this entirely superseding the one previously issued. Thus, for week commencing 14th July (see Table) the sales requirement is 50 units, of which 20 are already in process, this leaving 30 to make. This method of recording is simplicity itself, and the small amount of time necessary to make the entries upon the table is well spent. As before mentioned, the two methods described are recommended only when production is uniform and the volume of work is comparatively small, but there are many factories in which these conditions prevail, and it is to these that the foregoing will probably be of value.

(g) A Repetition Job

Some factories, though to all intents and purposes concerned with one specific line of manufacture, are nevertheless interested in what might be termed a side line, introduced for the purpose of keeping certain of the more rapid production machines fully employed.

To give a concrete case, in one factory where a fairly large number of automatic machines were installed for the handling of certain of the component parts comprising the unit, it was found that the production of these machines exceeded the requirement, and with a view to keeping them fully employed without filling the store with unwanted details, the management solicited work of a repetition character from other manufacturers.

It was not a difficult matter to get work suitable for these machines but it was difficult to get work that could be completed on these machines; that is, work upon which no further operations were necessary. In the case under review, the most satisfactory contract that could be secured covered a large number of small details which necessitated, apart from automatic work, a milling operation and a minor assembling operation.

It was not considered necessary to install additional milling machines to cope with this requirement, whilst the assembling operation could easily be handled by two boys. It was decided, therefore, to undertake this work, and a first order was received for 18,000 sets.

That the progress man found plenty to do in connection with this work will be realized when the summary of his activities, on pages 164 and 166, is read. It will be seen that, although the side line was introduced to keep certain machines fully employed, there were times when these machines could not cope with the demand, and it will also be seen that delays occurred in the milling section, on account of the priority given to standard manufactures. Too often the side line is introduced without sufficient attention being paid to the probable effect upon the standard manufacture, for although to all intents and purposes the latter takes precedence, it is forgotten that a certain output must be maintained in the case of the contract which constitutes the "side line." This is, however, brought forcibly to the mind of the management when the customer commences to shout, and it is then that ordinary production suffers whilst an endeavour is made to work off arrears.

The progress man is expected to see that output is maintained in accordance with the programme, so far as ordinary manufacture is concerned, for any failure here is reflected in a diminished output for the assembling shop. At the same time he must see that the promises given in connection with the "side line" are kept, and this is a more difficult proposition, for whilst in regard to ordinary manufacture he has the active assistance of every foreman (each of whom is as much concerned as the progress man in working to the programme) that assistance is entirely lacking in the case of the "side line." The foreman steadfastly refuses to handle the latter until his ordinary commitments are discharged, and as these are in most cases sufficient to keep his section fully employed, the prospects of the "side line" are not very bright.

The following summary, compiled a few years ago by a progress man in connection with an actual job, shows fairly clearly the difficulties encountered, and the steps taken to obviate or minimize them—

30th March.	Report given to Works Manager, this showing the present position of the contract. Promise made to complete the contract by 17th June. Works Manager reduces this by two weeks.
2nd April.	411 rejected by Inspector, and returned to works for rectification.
7th April.	First 2,000 dispatched.
10th April.	1,000 pieces in View Room. Inspector promises 500 by 5 p.m. Arranged with Machine Shop Foreman to increase output from the Auto Section, by putting another machine into commission.
12th April.	Present position: 400 assembling, 300 inspecting, 400 milling, 300 ready for milling.
	Advised Machine Shop Foreman that all milling machines are working on standard production. Foreman replies that standard production takes precedence. Reported this to Works Manager.
14th April.	Works Manager complains that deliveries are too small. Machine Shop Foreman promises to deliver 2,000 weekly.
15th April.	Advised Works Manager that milling operation was lagging.
16th April.	Spoke to Machine Shop Foreman on the same matter, who stated that he could not improve.
17th April.	Foreman fitter advises that 2,000 will be ready to time.
18th April.	Asked Stores for further supplies of raw material.
19th April.	2,000 dispatched.
26th April.	,,
29th April.	Owing to large number of rejects, 1,000 only will be dispatched this week.
3rd May.	1,000 dispatched.
8th May.	Assembling lagging. Saw foreman, who promised that 2,000 would be ready by end of week. Advised Works Manager.
10th May.	Advised Works Manager that assemblers are falling farther behind, due to the rejection of a large number of parts.
15th May.	3,000 dispatched.
18th May.	Milling Section behind. Advised Machine Shop Foreman.
22nd May.	2,000 dispatched.
24th May.	1,000 parts in Assembling Section rejected by Inspector. New gauge to be made. Advised Works Manager.
28th May.	All parts to be tested to new gauge.
31st May.	Replace material for completion of machining received.
3rd June.	14,000 have now passed final inspection.

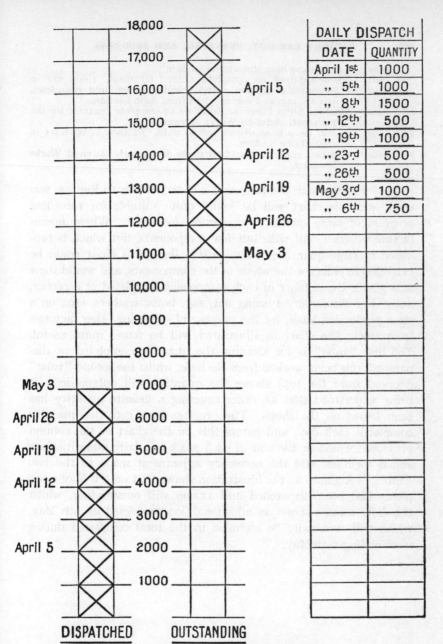

DAILY DISPATCH	
DATE	QUANTITY
April 1st	1000
,, 5th	1000
,, 8th	1500
,, 12th	500
,, 19th	1000
,, 23rd	500
,, 26th	500
May 3rd	1000
,, 6th	750

DISPATCHED   **OUTSTANDING**

PRODUCTION CHART

EXPLANATION

NUMBER DISPATCHED TO 3RD MAY
(Reading from bottom), 7,000

NUMBER OUTSTANDING ON 3RD MAY
(Reading from top), 11,000

FIG. 44

8th June.   14,000 have been dispatched to date.

9th June.   4,000 required to complete order. Of these, 1,000 are in Assembling Section, 2,000 Viewing (machining complete), 400 Milling, and 600 required from Auto Section.

12th June.   Machine Shop Foreman promises to complete contract by the 15th inst. Advised Works Manager.

18th June.   16,000 have been dispatched to date. Balance of contract in Assembling Section.

25th June.   Contract completed and all parts dispatched. Advised Works Manager.

In connection with the foregoing a chart, similar to Fig. 44, was used, and this chart will be found quite suitable for recording progress of large quantity production for stock. Where manufacture covers a unit with but few components, but which is produced in large quantities on repetition lines, this chart could be extended to embrace the whole of the components, and would show at a glance the number of each component completed at a certain date. For the factory turning out, say, bolts, washers, etc., on a mass production basis, for the purpose of supplying other factories from stock, the chart as illustrated will be found quite useful. The first "tube" is for showing the quantity completed or dispatched, this being worked from the base, whilst the second "tube" (worked from the top) shows the quantity still outstanding, it being understood that an order covering a definite quantity has been issued on the shops. The progress man gets the quantity completed each day, and enters this on the chart in the column provided; whilst at the end of each week the daily quantities are added together, and the necessary adjustment made to the two "tubes." A glance at the illustration shows that on 3rd May 7,000 pieces had been dispatched and 11,000 still outstanding, whilst the daily column shows an additional 600 completed on 6th May, which will eventually be included in the total completed during week ending 10th May.

CHAPTER IX

PROGRESS REPORTS AND STATEMENTS

(a) The Necessity for Prompt and Accurate Information

THE up-to-date works manager recognizes the value of prompt and accurate information, although he is not disposed to maintain a large clerical staff to ensure this. On the contrary, he is convinced that the man whose duty is mainly that of "investigating" is the individual best qualified for the task, and as a consequence it is the progress man who is called upon to supply the information.

This aspect must not therefore be disregarded, and in this connection a warning may be extended to the progress man who disdains the use of a pencil and note-book, and is content to rely upon his memory, for memory (at its best) is not infallible, and the manager has a knack of asking awkward questions at times. A simple inquiry, involving a couple of sentences, is easily answered, but the demand for a detailed report is not so easily complied with. Whilst slavish devotion to elaborate records forms no part of the writer's creed, he is deeply sensible to the advantages that accrue from a brief yet methodical résumé of daily happenings, and would urge the reader's acceptance of this principle.

Not only, however, is the progress man asked to compile a report, but he is often expected to assume the initiative, with a view to keeping the manager informed. Such a report must not, of course, be compiled merely for the sake of appearances, nor yet with the sole view of bringing the delinquencies of other people to the notice of the higher authorities. A report, to be effective, must be concerned with a matter of real importance, and it must be accurate. The spirit of the organization in regard to unsolicited reports should be that "no news is good news," although this does not mean that a sense of false security should be engendered by the withholding of bad news.

The basis of the report is the record, which is compiled from documents and oral statements. Whilst the former are in themselves a guarantee for accuracy (from the standpoint of the compiler of the record), the oral statement is an elusive quantity that requires careful handling. It is an easy matter for a man to make a statement, only to repudiate it at a later date, and it is an easy matter too, for a statement to be wrongly interpreted. Yet it is impossible to commit every statement to writing, whilst it is only in comparatively few instances that the recipient of an oral statement feels constrained to send out a written confirmation. The oral statement must be admitted as evidence, otherwise the clerical organization of the factory would become top-heavy, with an expense disproportionate to the services rendered.

It is in this connection that the value of the *résumé* of daily happenings is apparent, for the record which is the outcome of this policy is convincing, even though it is mainly comprised of oral statements. Taking the progress sheet relating to a specific order as the record referred to, we read that the order was received on a certain date, and that full instructions were issued to the factory three days later, both statements being substantiated by documentary evidence. Then we read that on the 5th inst. no material had been received from the store, that the storekeeper was seen on that date, and that he promised to deliver on the 6th inst. The next entry tells us that the material reached the shops on the 7th inst., and that work was taken in hand immediately upon receipt of material. On the 10th inst. we read that the first operation is completed, and on the 12th inst. that the second operation cannot be taken in hand owing to another order having preference. The entry on the 13th gives the same information, together with the fact that the head foreman had been approached, and had promised to complete the second operation on the 16th inst. Subsequent entries show that the second operation was not completed until the 18th, that the job went into the view room on that date, but did not come out until the 21st; that the third operation was taken in hand on the 21st, but that, on the following day, the jig was sent to the tool room for repair, and was not ready until the 25th, the operation being delayed in consequence. So the entries appear upon the sheet until the job is completed and actually dispatched, forming a complete record of progress and delays; and the manager, demanding a report, could at any time have the very latest information at his disposal.

It is quite unlikely that any foreman would challenge such a record, for a sequence of short date entries relating even to oral statements does not permit of argument. Where a number of days elapse between two entries bearing upon the same matter, or where the last entry relating to a specific circumstance is inconclusive, there is always the danger of the record being contested, and it behoves the progress man therefore to marshall his facts with a view to preventing any loophole.

Not long ago the managing director of an important industrial concern expressed a wish to see the progress office records, and was in the first instance shown a chart giving particulars of the number of completed units dispatched, and the number actually in hand for final erection. He then wished to know the precise stage of progress reached by the units which were not far enough advanced to appear upon the chart, and was shown a table setting out the whole of the operations involved in the correct sequence, those operations completed being indicated by means of a date entry. He was thus able to glean the following information, viz.: First operation completed 6/9. Second operation completed 10/9, and so on, up to last operation (prior to final erection) completed 14/10. Then (from the chart), in hand for final erection 20/10, and completed and dispatched 31/10.

So far so good, but he was not altogether satisfied. Was it possible for the progress man to show why the first operation was not completed before 10th Sept., and why two weeks elapsed between the completion of the 4th and 5th operations? The daily *résumé*, in the form of a progress sheet, was then submitted, and this gave all the particulars asked for, in substantially the same manner as recorded earlier in this chapter. The progress man was able to assert, without hesitation, that at any time he could give the complete history of any job in the factory, up to within two hours of the time of the inquiry.

But whilst the record is invaluable, it is of course obvious that the compiling of records is by no means the most important of the progress man's duties. It is true that, just as some men insist that they have no time for making notes, their whole attention being engaged upon the problem of keeping the work moving, others will go to the other extreme, and spend practically the whole of their time in faithfully recording what has happened and what has not happened. Their own influence upon the circumstance is apparently nil, and when the manager reads that on 9th Sept. material had not been received from the store, this announcement being repeated on the 12th and again on the 15th; whilst on 18th Sept. is an entry to the effect that material has been received, he is constrained to ask what the progress man was doing in the interval, and whether he could not have facilitated matters had he devoted more attention to progress and less to the record. Instead of the above, the following reading would be far more satisfying. "9th Sept., waiting material. Saw storekeeper, who promised to deliver by 5 p.m.; 10th Sept., material received and first operation in hand." This shows that the progress man has achieved something, in addition to recording the circumstance for future reference; and if he will recognize that his real business is to restrict detail by making it unnecessary, so far as he is able, the progress man's record will be the more convincing, because it gives due prominence, not only to real difficulties, but also to his own efforts to combat them.

Having thus dealt with the spirit in which the record should be compiled, we can now consider how it may be used to the best advantage. It is agreed that every detail must be strictly accurate, and it must also be quite impartial. In an industrial factory there are a number of conflicting interests, usually of a departmental character. The head of each department is concerned wholly and solely with his department, and there is a good deal of "putting the blame elsewhere" when trouble is in the air. As a consequence, there is a certain amount of bad feeling (professionally, of course) between the heads of the various departments, and comments similar to the following are often heard: "He considers he is in the right every time," "He takes too much upon himself," "He has 'twisted' me, and will 'twist' you, if he can," and so on. It is but natural that the progress man (as a human being) will "taken to one individual more than to another, but he must not be drawn into any little quarrel, and his attitude must not be marked by bias. Once let it be known that his report favours one department at the expense of another (and particularly if both are equally culpable) and he finds himself up against trouble. He must be scrupulously fair in all his dealings, trusting to his own eyes rather than to the glasses of other people, and he cannot fail to win respect.

(b) Examples of Reports

Using information to the best advantage should be a great point with the progress man, but unfortunately it is not always so. One individual was an adept in gathering information, but he was a dullard in the art of "passing it on." In the first place, he appeared to consider it a crime to hand to the manager an unsolicited report, and in the second (when asked for a report) he lacked the art of condensing, and set out on paper, in the fullest detail, the whole of the information he had acquired. Such a "report" was useless to the busy manager, who either turned it down or sent for the man in order to get an intelligible explanation.

It is understood that no manager likes to be worried with petty details, and it is not necessary that he should be. On the other hand, it must be borne in mind that a matter may assume different proportions from the viewpoint of the manager than from that of the progress man. To put this in other words, what appears important to the progress man may appear trivial to the manager, or *vice versa*. In regard to this the difficulty is only overcome by close association, during which time the progress man becomes familiar with the methods and the characteristics of the manager, and can act accordingly.

We have before asserted that the progress man is not merely a compiler of records, but is an active and intelligent individual, whose proficiency in his profession is unquestioned. It is this proficiency which enables him to use the information he has obtained to the best advantage, and this applies particularly to the unsolicited report.

It is of no use waiting until the delivery date has expired before acquainting the manager of particulars of the delay, for at this stage his intervention is useless, save only for the purpose of minimizing the delay. On the other hand, there is nothing gained in apprising him (a week or so prior to the date of delivery) of an impending delay, unless its nature is such as to suggest to the progress man that it cannot be averted by his own unaided effort. During the course of a job, many delays occur—some trivial, others more serious—but, until the job arrives at its concluding stages, there is always the possibility of an early delay being made good by the speeding up of subsequent stages.

It is in this connection that the progress man must use discretion. and his knowledge of the job should enable him to do the right thing, The order taken on a quick delivery basis must be expeditiously handled at all stages, and even the slightest delay may adversely affect the delivery date. In such a case prompt notification must be given to the management, but only after all interested officials have been interviewed, and it is reasonably certain that delay cannot be avoided unless extraordinary measures are employed. These measures may comprise overtime, or the dropping of another job in order to give preferential treatment to the one in question, and for such measures to be employed the sanction of the manager is necessary. It is not enough to notify the manager that a delay will occur—he must know the reason, and how (if possible) it can be obviated. The following may be quoted as an example of a report sent to the manager in these circumstances—

To Works Manager.   From Progress Department.   Sept. 24th

Job No. 3743.   1. C.I. Bracket.   Due for delivery Sept. 28th

There is a probability of delivery date being exceeded owing to the scrapping of the cap, due to blowholes. Replacement has been put in hand, and is promised from the foundry to-morrow (the 25th inst.). Machine shop foreman requires three days after receipt of casting, and the fitter two days after receipt of machined parts. The foreman of the machining and fitting departments advise that, by working overtime, the original delivery date can be kept; otherwise, it must be extended to the 30th inst.

Upon receipt of this report, the manager takes action. It may be that he has a few days "up his sleeve" in regard to delivery, so that the extension can be allowed, and he therefore instructs the progress man that delivery on the 30th inst. will be accepted, but that the date in question must on no account be exceeded. On the other hand, it may be necessary for him to take active measures to ensure the original date being kept, and in the first instance he considers the recommendation offered, viz. overtime. He may be satisfied with this, and give his sanction without comment, but overtime not being in favour these days, it is more likely he will try some other expedient. He will want to know why the machine shop foreman requires three days for machining, and on investigating this will probably find that a delay in connection with another job will not be a serious matter, and that the holding back of this job at a certain stage will allow of the replacement coming forward and being completed in time to meet the original date. The progress man, however, has done his duty in presenting the report and embodying the recommendation, but the decision of the manager should be entered upon his record for future reference, and, if any other job is involved, the circumstance should appear upon the record of that job also.

Sometimes the progress man has a presentiment that a delay will occur, despite assurances to the contrary, and whether or not to take action (by voicing his fears) requires deep consideration. It may be said that, if the progress man is in possession of a promise given by a person in authority, he must assume that that promise will be kept, and not set his judgment against that of the head of a department. This, of course, may sound feasible enough, and after all, it is the easiest line of resistance, but the duty of the progress man is to keep a sharp look out, and give the alarm at the slightest symptom of danger. How he gives the alarm must be left to his own discretion—he may let drop a hint in the hearing of the manager that matters are not as well as they appear, or he may adopt the more straightforward course of making a definite statement in writing.

In this, however, he must take care not to earn the character of a scaremonger, yet on the other hand he must not feel (because his fears have, upon investigation, been proved groundless) that the easiest line of resistance is the best course to follow. In many cases trouble at a later date is avoided by prompt action on the part of the progress man, although that action at the time appeared superfluous. In one instance the progress man (guided by past experience) reported to the manager at the commencement of a job that there was danger of an abnormal amount of scrap developing, and suggested the manufacture of a certain percentage of details over and above the quantity on order, so as to ensure the order being completed without having to wait for replacements. After investigation, the suggestion was "turned down," and in due course the job was completed without the progress man's fears being realized. Yet it was in a great measure due to his intervention that the trouble did not materialize, for the knowledge that (as a result of the report) the manager was keeping close watch upon the job caused the factory officials to adopt more rigid measures with a view to obviating scrap.

The example given on the next page is of a report compiled in somewhat similar circumstances.

To Works Manager.   From Progress Department.   25th Sept.

Job No. 3782.   1 Type J Unit.   Due for delivery 5th Oct.

I submit for your consideration the following—

Part No. 31572 will be the limiting feature on this job, and may possibly prevent the delivery date being kept. This part will be out of the Automatic Department on the 28th inst., and must then undergo the following operations, viz. Milling (two operations), Drilling, Hardening, Grinding. Promises have been given by the various foremen, which should result in the part being in the hands of the fitter by the 3rd ultimo, in which case the unit will be ready for dispatch on 5th October. Bearing in mind the troubles we have previously experienced in connection with similar parts, I am afraid that, unless the utmost attention is given at every stage, certain of these promises will not be kept, and the slightest delay, in either machining or hardening, will adversely affect the delivery date. I would suggest therefore that a letter (signed by the Works Manager) be sent to each of the foremen concerned, emphasizing the extreme importance of the job, and insisting upon each promise made being strictly adhered to.

In the factory where the progress department occupies a preeminent position, it would not be necessary for such a report to be addressed to the works manager, but it would be addressed by the progress man to his chief, whose position would enable him to comply with the suggestion. In the smaller factory, however, it is the works manager who is regarded as the only authority by the works officials, and in such circumstances a recommendation which must be carried out by means of an order must obviously be addressed to the one person who has authority to give that order.

We can now deal with what may be termed "solicited reports," of which there are many variations. Some of these relate to one specific job, others to a number of jobs in process of manufacture, whilst in some instances reports are asked for on matters of more general interest, such as particulars of the commitments of certain departments, etc. The first example is in respect to a daily report sent by the progress man to the sales office, confined strictly to specific jobs enumerated by the sales office, the procedure being as follows.

Each morning a selection of orders to be reported upon is made by the sales office, and a list forwarded to the progress man, who is expected to deliver a brief report before the close of the day. The real question is one of delivery, and as far as possible definite dates must be given, together with brief particulars of the factors contributing to delay (if any). Upon receipt of the report, the sales manager raises any point he considers necessary, and marks upon the sales cards covered by the report the date upon which another demand is to be made upon the progress man, assuming that the job is not completed in the meantime. For example, if on the 20th inst., the progress man reports that the job will be completed on the 25th inst., that same job will appear on the demand issued on the following day (the 26th) assuming that the promise was not kept, and the progress man is then expected to give the precise reasons of delay. A progress report sent to the sales office is given below—

To Sales Office.   From Progress Office.   26th Sept.

Please note the following in connection with your list of to-day's date—

Order 3742. Details for Type K Unit. This was promised for the 25th inst., but delayed owing to trouble with Hook and Eye in Machine Shop. The parts are now completed, and the job will be dispatched without fail to-morrow (the 27th inst.).

Order 3781. Type L Unit. The dial is on order outside. Have telephoned suppliers to-day, who promise to dispatch per passenger train on the 3rd ultimo. All other details will be completed to-morrow, and if the dial is received on 4th October, the unit will be dispatched on 6th October.

Order 3784. Type L Unit. Purchasing Department advise that estimate for dial confirmed to-day, and order has been placed. Suppliers promise is three weeks from date. Other details in hand in factory.

Order 3790. 10 Type J Units. Due for delivery 17th October. Work is well in hand, and delivery date should be kept

Order 3791. 2 Type V Units. Full specification not yet to hand. Drawing Office require one week to complete.

There are times when, despite every precaution, the stocks of the various component parts of a unit are not proportionate, or, in other words, the stocks of components do not represent the number of units that can be assembled. In the case which has been chosen as an example, the manager was not satisfied with the factory weekly output, and elicited from the progress man the fact that the trouble was due to the irregularity of supplies from the foundry. He therefore asked for a report concerning the stocks of the three main structural castings for each model, together with particulars of future requirements, with a view to issuing a foundry department programme. The report he received was as follows—

To Works Manager. From Progress Department. 27th September.

The stocks of structural castings for each model are as follows—

Type of Assembly	Bases	Frames	Brackets
Vw	101	53	189
Vx	48	168	180
Vz	109	89	183

With these we can assemble—

Vw 53,   Vx 48,   Vz 89.   Total 190.

With an output of 40 Units per week, this represents just under 5 weeks' work
Further supplies of castings are required in the following order—

Vx	Bases	120
Vz	Frames	100
Vz	Bases	80
Vw	Frames	100

Then a minimum of 40 complete sets for each model weekly.

One factory was engaged upon the manufacture of an assembled unit in two sizes, but output was low owing to the difficulty in getting sufficient supplies of castings, which had to be purchased outside. To get over the trouble, extra patterns were made, with a view to extending the list of suppliers, but work in this connection was somewhat protracted. The manager asked for a report on the general situation, and received one similar to the following—

To Works Manager.   From Progress Department.   9th September.

Report on Castings for Types 14A and 14B Units.

Type 14A.   There are in the factory 72 Cases and 102 Stands.

,,   Cases.   We are getting 10 per week from Black & Co., and 5 per week from General Foundry. New wood pattern is at X Foundry, and iron-working patterns are promised by the end of the week.

,,   Stands.   All new patterns are now in commission, and adequate supplies of castings are being maintained.

Type 14B.   There are in the factory 174 Cases and 94 Stands.

,,   Cases.   Blank & Co. are delivering castings at the rate of 30 per week. They have 3 patterns in use.
A new working pattern will be ready on the 12th inst., and will be sent to the General Foundry. This foundry will deliver 10 castings weekly. Two more new patterns will be ready in 2 weeks from date, and when these are available, the General Foundry will deliver 30 castings weekly.

,,   Stands.   Two new patterns have been sent to Blank & Co., who promise to deliver 80 per week, commencing next week.

A report concerning a specific job is compiled from the progress sheet, and is "backed up" by documentary evidence wherever possible. It may be that, a week or more after the order has been executed, a report is demanded by the works manager, this following adverse comments from the sales manager regarding the time taken by the factory to complete the job, and especially when the accepted delivery date has been exceeded. It is impossible for the progress man to prepare a reliable report in these circumstances, unless the daily happenings in connection with the job have been duly recorded, and when this is the case, a report similar to the following can be easily compiled.

To Works Manager.   From Progress Department.   29th October.
Report on Job Number 4161. 1 Type Y Electric Motor.
Order dated 1st Sept. Due for dispatch 27th September.
Complete Specification received 6th Sept.

Stator	*Rotor*
Special Laminations received 10th Sept.	Shaft Material received 7th Sept.
	Shaft completed 17th Sept.
Core assembled and sent to Winding Dept., 12th Sept.	(Delay 3 days in Grinding Section, due to pressure of work)
Winding completed 25th Sept.	Core assembled and sent to Winding Dept. 20th Sept.
(Delay. No Terminals in stock.	Winding completed 26th Sept.
Received 24th Sept.)	Slip-rings fitted 28th Sept.
	Slip-rings balanced 29th Sept.
	Rotor complete 29th Sept.

Motor assembled and sent to Test Dept. 2nd Oct.
Returned from test (open circuit) 4th Oct.
Motor dismantled and Stator sent to Winding Dept. 5th Oct.
Stator returned from Winding Dept. 8th Oct.
Motor re-assembled and sent to Test Dept. 9th Oct.
Motor sent to Dispatch Dept. 11th Oct.
Order dispatched 11th Oct.

From the foregoing it will be seen that the failure of the unit to pass the test is the chief cause of the delay, but it would not be right to charge the whole of the delay to this factor, seeing that, had the unit passed test, there would still have been a delay, though not, of course, of the same magnitude. It is advisable in such circumstances to enumerate every factor, leaving it to the manager to apportion the culpability of the departments concerned.

(c) A Statement

It may be necessary from time to time to issue a statement, showing the output from a certain department during a given period, in order to ascertain whether or not the requirements are being met. It is not always possible for a direct yes or no to be given on the spur of the moment, for although there may be delays in connection with given details, it may be that an excess of other parts has been put through, this bringing the aggregate up to the maximum.

It may be argued that if the issue of work is efficiently planned, this will automatically obviate the possibility of any excess, seeing that the orders issued will cover such work as is actually required.

This, however, is far from being the case, and many instances may be advanced to prove that the difficulty is not overcome in this manner. The following have been selected for the purposes of illustration.

We are assuming that the department in question is responsible for sets of details, not assembled together, but ready (after this department's operation has been completed) to be assembled. It is not possible for the parts to be sent to the department in question actually in sets, owing to circumstances governing the previous operations, and even in the department in question it is considered expedient to handle the details in varying quantities, according to the size of the articles and the amount of work entailed.

In other words, although so far as some details are concerned, the exact number required can be put in hand each week, it is a more economical proposition in the case of others for these to be put through in larger quantities than those actually required. In regard to these latter then, two, three, or four weeks' requirements are put into process at one time, it being understood that a second batch of similar parts will not be handled until the period covering the first batch has elapsed.

Assuming the weekly requirement to be fifty, and that a four weeks' supply of a given detail could be put in hand at once, this would make the quantity 200, and an order for that number would be issued, whilst at the expiration of four weeks an order would be issued for a further 200. During the intervening weeks there would be no orders issued for further supplies of this specific detail, but there would be orders for other details being handled in a similar manner. Fig. 45 gives a clear illustration of the case in point.

For the output of the department to be commensurate with the intake, it is necessary for all parts received into the department this week to be completed and delivered back to store during the succeeding week. As a matter of fact, in many cases it is not at all necessary for the output to be equal to the intake, as often extra parts are sent in merely as "stop gaps," and work on these parts ceases when the more important details come along.

What *is* necessary is that the output is in accordance with the estimate, and as the estimated weekly output is fifty sets of parts per week, then the aggregate number of parts represented by these sets must be handled. In other words, assuming that fifty sets total 1,000 parts, then this number must be dealt with, and it is the business of the progress man to ensure that the 1,000 parts sent to the department represent sets as far as possible.

Another point is that all orders for the week are not issued upon one specific day, neither is one day set apart for the return of the details to the store. Orders may be made out in advance as far as possible, but as the department in question is responsible for the last operation, it is obvious that any delay in the preceding operations will be felt here. The progress man should be able to gauge fairly accurately, but he cannot anticipate every delay, and often

ORDER			ORDER			ORDER		
X Dept.		8th Oct.	X Dept.		15th Oct.	X Dept.		22nd Oct.
		Part No.			Part No.			Part No.
50	Base	116	50	Base	116	50	Base	116
100	Guard	119	200	Collar	123	100	Guard	119
50	Bracket	121	50	Bracket	121	50	Bracket	121
50	Frame	102	50	Frame	102	50	Frame	102
200	Rod	108	100	Support	109	200	Knob	115
100	Pin	103	100	Connection	114	100	Pin	103
200	Bearing	126	200	Hook	118	200	Handle	125
	1st Week			*2nd Week*			*3rd Week*	

FIG. 45

he will refrain from issuing "stop gap" orders until the work is actually required, in the hope that the correct detail will be ready.

This makes it possible, unless care is taken, for a smaller issue than fifty sets being made in one week, for the foreman will not ask for orders unless he actually wants work. As it is the duty of the progress department to take the initiative, and in a way force the foreman to take the amount of work predetermined, a short issue is a serious matter, yet is not easily detected when the aggregate number of details constitutes a high figure.

Further confusion also arises when it is remembered that returns are being made daily, and there is a possibility of later orders being executed first. Some parts are much more easily handled than others, and there is a tendency for these parts to be dealt with first, irrespective of the relative degree of urgency. The compilation of a statement at certain periods will speedily detect any such case, and will also show what work has been neglected to allow for this being done.

It is often the case that the more intricate work arrives in the department at the last moment, this despite every precaution, and extraordinary efforts have to be made to ensure this being completed by the time required. This does not necessarily mean that insufficient time is allowed, but it is quite possible that the work clashes with other work of equal importance, and when this happens there is grave danger of one or the other job being allowed to stand over. The department may be planned very efficiently, and if the work comes through in the correct sequence it can be handled expeditiously, but the correct sequence means that the intricate

X Dept. INTAKE AND OUTPUT during Five Weeks Oct. 13–Nov. 10

Part No.	Description	Require-ment	Intake	Output
102	Frame	250	200	197
103	Pin	250	300	300
104	Roller	500	500	390
105	Spindle	500	450	510
106	Cap	250	300	300
108	Rod	250	400	300
109	Support	250	300	250
114	Connection . . .	250	300	310
115	Knob	250	400	200
116	Base	250	250	230
118	Hook	500	400	450
119	Guard	250	200	250
121	Bracket . . .	250	250	250
123	Collar	500	400	500
125	Handle	250	200	200
126	Bearing	250	400	300

Fig. 46

jobs are spread over the week, being intermingled with jobs of simpler proportions.

In theory these troubles do not occur, but in practice they are frequent. We aim at prevention, but what we cannot prevent we must cure, or at least minimize the ill effects. It is quite possible for the issue clerk to say that all orders have been issued correctly, and for the department foreman to say that he has completed the prescribed number of details, yet both may be wrong. In one argument the foreman asserted that he was *not* handling the amount of work required, whilst the progress man took the opposite view. The statement, illustrated by Fig. 46, was compiled to settle the matter, and it was found that the foreman was wrong.

The statement is made to cover a period of five weeks, and shows the name of the detail, the requirement, the number issued, and the number completed. This period allows for the recording of the smaller parts which are handled in bulk, as previously explained, for a weekly chart or statement would not give a correct impression. The issue figures are compiled from the orders actually issued, whilst the returns are taken from the delivery notes signed by the storekeeper.

The statement shows at a glance if there has been a lapse in the matter of issues, or whether there has been an excess, and the cases may be investigated. It may be that, in certain instances, there is a large stock of parts, and it is not considered necessary to place further orders until this stock is somewhat reduced, whilst the progress man must use his discretion in the matter of placing excess orders for other parts to bring the aggregate number up to the estimate. The statement is valuable, inasmuch as after a perusal any trouble may be located, and a correct estimate formed.

CHAPTER X

WHAT TO DO

(a) To Ensure Operations being Handled in the Correct Sequence

WHEN a progress man is concerned with one specific class of apparatus, whilst other progress men are concerned with other classes, it often happens that the jobs of two men clash, or, in other words, an order in which one man is interested reaches a certain stage at precisely the same time as the order belonging to the other fellow, and both cannot be handled simultaneously. This occurs particularly in the machining department, when this department handles the machining of details associated with every class of apparatus, and there is often a good deal of argument concerning the sequence in which these jobs shall be handled.

The best method of avoiding trouble in this connection is for each progress man to hand to the chief each morning a brief list of the orders required from each machining section, and for the chief to arrange the order in which they shall be handled. This method is helpful to the individual progress man, and also to the section foremen, but it is practicable only in the smaller type of factory, on account of the work it means for the progress chief. In the larger factory a mutual arrangement could be entered into by the various progress men, resulting in the issue of a priority list, the factors entering into consideration being (a) the date of delivery, (b) the length of the operation, and (c) the nature and length of subsequent operations.

Failing an arrangement similar to the foregoing, it is fairly obvious that the persistent man will score, so long as his persistency does not render him obnoxious to the foreman. Some men delight to score over their colleagues, and are not over scrupulous in the methods they employ, but there is really no sense in rushing through a job that can afford to wait at the expense of one that cannot, simply because the first happens to be one's own job, whilst the other belongs to another fellow. The active man naturally expects to achieve better results than his lazy colleague, but there is a difference between this very laudable ambition and the species of competition which emanates from a desire to "show off." The one makes for efficiency whilst the other leads to confusion, and whilst individualism may achieve temporary success, it is good team work that makes the wheels of progress revolve.

(b) To Get a "Part" Delivery

Avoid this state of affairs wherever possible by efficient progressing. If, despite every effort on the part of the progress man, it is apparent that a batch of work cannot be completed by the time the assemblers will require it, steps must be taken to effect a part delivery, if this is practicable.

Suppose the machining order covers a quantity of 500 pieces, and 100 will satisfy immediate requirements. What the progress man must do is to find out the present location and the state of the work, and what machining operations have yet to be handled. He must then approach the section foreman, emphasize the urgency of the matter, and suggest (not demand) that he finishes off 100 pieces in advance.

When these are to hand, it must be remembered that "short circuiting" the system will not help matters. The man who rushes along with the advance quantity, ignoring the necessity for notification and inspection, intent only upon getting the parts to the assembling shop, is simply asking for trouble, and will in all probability cause a good deal of delay a little later. If each operation is to be inspected, let him take the parts to the inspecting room, and when the quantity is signed for by the inspector upon the operator's work card, let him return that card to the section. If this is done, the exact quantity finished in advance will be known, and there will be no "shortage" trouble when the order is completed.

There may be some difficulty in persuading the various section foremen to handle the smaller quantity, for although the foreman who has the job actually in hand may consent to finish off a few, it is not so easy for the foreman of another section to disarrange his programme in order to accommodate a rush job. Still, if the request is put in a tactful way, there is no reason to anticipate failure, but it must be remembered that, although tact may do it, bluster will not. The small quantity is an uneconomical proposition, from a machining standpoint, and no foreman likes to see excessive production charges scored against his section. The only excuse that can be made is that failure to get the parts to the assembling shop by the date required will result in even heavier expense, and it is necessary for all concerned to endeavour to obviate this. However, deliveries in advance must be kept down to a minimum, otherwise they will seriously impair the efficiency of the organization. Smart progressing in the early stages will have a beneficial effect here.

(c) To Minimize Delay Arising out of Misplaced Documents

In many factories the routine states that the operator's work card or a production card must accompany every job to the view room, and the viewer is advised to refuse to accept work unless this condition is complied with. Sometimes the card cannot be found when the job is ready for inspection, and a delay follows unless the progress man is early on the track, for no one else will interest himself in the matter. The foreman responsible for the operation just completed is more concerned with the follow-up job than with the dispatch of completed work, whilst the inspector, liable to be criticized later on owing to the time a job is kept in his department, will naturally refuse to accept work which he cannot deal with.

When a labourer is told off to convey jobs to the view room, he must see that the necessary cards are there, and should one be missing, his duty is to acquaint the progress man concerned without delay. Assuming a production card to be missing, the progress man must first consider in what departments (and under what conditions) the card may be located, and the departments to come up for review may be as follows—

(a) The Progress Office.   Whilst operations are in progress.
(b) The Rate-fixing Office. When operations or rates are being adjusted.
(c) The Inspection Dept.   When part or complete deliveries have been made.
(d) The Component Store.   When part or complete deliveries of finished components have been made.

His knowledge of the job should enable the progress man to determine the department most likely to be in possession of the card. Really, it *should* be in the progress office, and because it cannot be located it does not follow that it is not there. It may have got out of its sequence in the file, and so the clerk is instructed to search for it. In the meantime, the progress man has decided that, as no part deliveries have been made against the order, the card cannot be in either the inspection department or the store, but it may be in the rate-fixing department, and it is in this direction that he pursues his inquiries. If the search fails to locate the card, the next move is to issue an emergency card, in order that the job may go through without future delay. This emergency card takes the place of the original until the latter once more turns up, as it is sure to do.

(d) When Certain Items are Suspended or Cancelled

It often happens, when many items are involved in the manufacture of a special unit, that modifications and amendments to the design are frequent, and unless these are dealt with promptly there is danger of confusion arising. We have elsewhere considered the handling of hold-ups, releases, and cancellations, but a few remarks here will not be out of place, as showing the progress man what to do when items on the specification list are cancelled or amended.

(a) If cancelled, delete the item on the specification list and progress sheet. Ascertain what work (if any) has been done, and have it inspected up to the last operation done. Make out a delivery note, and send the part to the store. The inspector should state whether the part is good stock, or scrap, and the stores should credit accordingly. Advise all foremen interested to send to the issuing office all unused operation cards relating to the part cancelled.

(b) If amended, make the necessary alterations upon the specification list and the progress sheet. Obtain drawings of both the old and the new parts in order to ascertain the extent of the change. If material has been issued and certain operations done, find out from the inspector if the part can still be utilized. If it cannot, return to store in the manner described above, and requisition a further supply of material.

If the change is promptly handled, it may be effected without the necessity for revising the delivery date for the completed unit. This, however, depends largely upon the effect the change will have upon sectional manufacture. For example, suppose that the shaft, upon which the rotor core is to be assembled, is to be replaced by a new one. In the ordinary course of events the rotor would be the limiting feature, and the change would tend to throw it still further behind. In these circumstances, the delivery date would have to be extended, and prompt notification should be sent to the works manager or the sales department (according to the procedure in vogue in the factory).

(e) To Handle Efficiently a Large Number of Special Orders in Process of Manufacture

It may appear, at first sight, a formidable undertaking for one man to be responsible for the progress of parts covered by 300 separate customers' orders, each of which must be completed by a pre-determined date, but when the matter is more closely investigated it will be found that, although the man does not get a deal of leisure, the task is not beyond the limit of his capabilities.

Each day new orders are received, and each day also old orders are cleared. Sometimes the daily intake exceeds the number completed, whilst at other times the reverse is the case, but over a period of, say, twelve months there is little variation in the aggregate of "live orders," each of which necessitates attention. Each order is dealt with on its merits—from a delivery standpoint. While some remain month after month, a "long date" being necessary owing to the intricacies of manufacture, others come and go with remarkable rapidity—those "short dated" orders that permit of no delay, and which demand unremitting attention during their short stay.

The method of handling governs the ability of the man to cope with such a huge volume of work, for the obviating of unnecessary action makes all the difference between success and failure. If one order is overlooked for a day or two, due to concentration upon another order, it is quite likely that progress remains stationary during that period, and later on a "rush" is necessary to meet the delivery date. "What to do" in order to ensure equitable treatment for every job may be outlined as follows.

As each order is received, make out a progress sheet, giving brief particulars of the work covered. The order may cover six 50 h.p. motors, for which hundreds of details are required, or it may cover but a spare shaft. There is no necessity to enumerate upon the progress sheet the whole of the details associated with the first order, as the bulk of these can probably be drawn from stock, so we can content ourselves with enumerating only those details upon which machining operations have yet to be done.

We have then, say, 300 progress sheets, each representing a separate order. Some of the jobs covered are now upon the point of completion, all operations save those associated with final assembling having been finished, so we can for the moment place the progress sheets connected with these jobs in a folder marked "Final Assembly." Other jobs will be ready for final assembling immediately two or three outstanding details are received from the machining department, and the progress sheets in this case may be placed in a folder marked "Machining." Still other jobs are being handled in the winding shop, whilst many of the more recent jobs have not yet left the core assembling section. The progress sheets are therefore placed in folders marked "Winding" and "Core Assembly" respectively.

Apart from the jobs mentioned above, there are many that cannot be catalogued so easily, owing to the necessity of speeding up details from more than one department. Each progress sheet will eventually come into one of the folders already classified, but to show how this comes about it will be necessary to describe the daily routine of the progress man. Before dealing with this, however, it may be well to remark that every new progress sheet covering an assembled unit is in the first instance placed in the folder marked "Core Assembly," whilst the new progress sheet covering spare parts upon which machining operations have to be performed, is placed in the folder marked "Machining." And now for the daily routine.

First of all the "Core Assembly" folder is handled, and all the progress sheets therein perused. The jobs covered may be classified thus: (a) New orders (i.e. those which have not previously been handled); (b) orders which are already in progress, and upon which definite promises for the completion of core assembling have been obtained; and (c) orders which to date have not been started in the core assembly, on account of certain items being required from other departments. Included in the latter category may be some of the new orders which require special laminations, etc.

A perusal of the sheets shows the progress man the orders he must deal with to-day. He will get a promise on those orders in classification (a) which do not require special parts, see the section foreman in regard to the orders (classification (b)) upon which the date for completion has expired, and get a promise from the section foreman in respect to those orders (classification (c)) where the outstanding parts have come to hand. To show this more plainly we will tabulate a few of the orders from the folder marked "Core Assembly," showing the outstanding feature in each case at the time the progress man peruses the sheets, and explain what action he should take.

			Action of Progress Man.
No. 1.	New order.	No special details required.	Obtain promise for the completion of core assembly.
No. 2.	New order.	Special lamination (due for completion in 3 days).	No action until three days have elapsed.
No. 3.	Old order.	Core assembly promised to complete yesterday.	See section foreman if promise has been kept. If so, mark sheet accordingly. If not, record reason of delay and obtain revised promise.
No. 4.	Old order.	Hitherto held for special laminations, which came to hand yesterday.	See section foreman, and obtain promise for completion of core assembly.
No. 5.	Old order.	Core assembly promised to complete in 2 days.	No action until completion date has expired.

When the progress man returns from his visit to the foreman of the core assembly section, he will find that his progress sheets need re-arranging. Some of them will remain in the core assembly folder for a further period, others will come out for a short space and then be returned, whilst the balance will be transferred to other folders. The first named include those orders in connection with which the date promised for completion has not yet expired, and those which are waiting for parts from other departments, but which are not yet due. The second named include those orders in connection with which details are wanted from other departments, and it is necessary to obtain promises from these departments. The final group comprises those orders that have been completed in the core assembly section, and forwarded to the winding shop; the progress sheets relating to these are therefore placed in the folder marked "Winding."

The next move of the progress man is to deal further with those orders in connection with which details are wanted from other departments, where promises have not yet been obtained, or, if obtained, have been exceeded. Those parts wanted from the machining department are not, however, dealt with at this stage, and the progress sheets are accordingly transferred to the folder marked "Machining," to be dealt with later, in conjunction with other orders affecting this department. The departments dealt with at this stage include the press shop, stores, etc., and satisfactory promises having been obtained and entered upon the progress sheets, the latter are again placed in the folder marked "Core Assembly."

The folder marked "Winding" is next dealt with, and the procedure followed is substantially the same as that already described. Those progress sheets relating to jobs which have left the winding shop are taken out and placed in the "Final Assembly" or the "Machining" folder, whichever is applicable, whilst those upon which promises have been obtained from the winding foreman remain in the folder marked "Winding."

The parts in process for machining are then handled, the procedure being in this instance to classify the progress sheets according to the machining sections, all progress sheets showing parts wanted from the turning section being together, and so on. In this connection there will probably be some quick shuffling, as on one progress sheet are parts wanted from each of two or three sections, but the real idea of this method is to arrange the sheets so that each section is visited by the progress man but once daily.

It may be that in some instances material is wanted by the machining departments from other departments, such as the foundry, etc., and these departments are next dealt with. When the round of visits is concluded, the progress sheets are placed in the appropriate folders, ready for the following day. It may be remarked here that the progress man, when obtaining promises, keeps the delivery date for the complete unit before him, and presses for a shorter date if he considers it necessary.

The folder marker "Final Assembly" is the last one dealt with, and when the completed units have passed into test the progress sheets are marked accordingly and filed for future reference.

CHAPTER XI

CONCLUSION

In drawing this work to a close, the author feels that he cannot do better than to dwell, for a moment or two, upon the personal side of the organization, in the relationship of the progress man with the various factory officials. The early days of the former, even in the well-organized factory, are such as to discourage any but the most determined, for the rebuffs are many, and the results of constant and conscientious application lamentably small. Lack of experience, when pitted against clever and competent officials, cuts a very sorry figure, and the contempt with which it is treated, even by those who are by no means antagonistic either to the individual, or to the branch of the organization of which he is a member, is a formidable obstacle to surmount. Good-natured ridicule and undisguised contempt both serve to bring home to the progress man his inferiority, and he must needs be a tenacious and determined individual if he would triumph over them.

Much depends upon the attitude he adopts, for whilst conscious lack of confidence is to be deplored, the blatantly confident individual is even more at a discount. This individual may have the hide of a rhinoceros, impervious alike to contempt and open insult, and he carries on in spite of all. He undoubtedly secures a certain measure of success, but his attitude alienates the goodwill of those with whom he comes into contact. His mistakes (and there must be many of these in the early stages of his career) excite derision, and although these are reduced as experience increases, he never enjoys the full measure of success, because he fails to secure co-operation and sympathy. He plays a "lone hand" because his associates are antagonistic, and, conscious of this, he wages perpetual warfare, which is not conducive to efficient organization.

The progress man who is quietly confident of ultimate success is fully conscious of his disabilities due to lack of experience, but repeated rebuffs make him but the more determined to succeed. He makes the fullest use of every circumstance, yet in a manner to which exception cannot be taken. He recognizes the status of those with whom he comes into contact, pays tribute to their experience and the position they occupy, and sets out to become worthy of their regard. Not that he fawns upon any one, nor yet does he turn the other cheek to the smiter. He is human enough to resent an open insult, and to retaliate; but his retaliation is with a view to turning an apparent enemy into a friend, and he usually succeeds.

The schoolboys' dictum "never sneak" is a most important factor, and will, if assiduously practised, do more than anything else to secure goodwill. To fight one's own battles without recourse to the authorities, and to meet a man upon his own ground, will inspire that respect which produces harmonious relations. The man who appeals to his chief upon each and every occasion; who bitterly complains of the treatment accorded him by this foreman and that foreman; who endeavours to fight that treatment by showing up the foreman in a bad light, will not make much headway, for he is despised, not only by his fellow-workers, but by the higher authorities also.

The young progress man will do well to practise patience, and not to stand too much "upon his dignity." When dealing with a foreman he must understand that he is dealing with a person who, by virtue of experience and proficiency, holds a responsible position, and he must be treated with respect, even though some of his actions may leave much to be desired. The progress man must not think he is entitled to a hearing, no matter at what time of the day he approaches a foreman, for the latter is a busy man, and cannot afford to be constantly called upon to supply information. Tact must be employed, and if the foreman is ostensibly engaged with another individual, it is better (unless the business is undeniably urgent) for the progress man to make a call elsewhere, rather than to interrupt the conversation, or to render himself conspicuous and thus catch the foreman's eye.

Sometimes the foreman will get rid of his questioner by sending him upon all sorts of impossible errands, whilst he may also (with the same end in view) give him information which is worthless or inaccurate. The inexperienced man cannot be expected to see the motive, and he naturally accepts at its face value, anything imparted to him; this, however, holds good for a short time only, for increasing experience will enable the progress man to sift the wheat from the chaff. Such tactics are only employed against inexperience, and the foreman is quick to discover when they will no longer pay. It is the attitude taken by the progress man in regard to these tactics that determines future relations; if he resents the "slight put upon his intelligence," he is not likely to make much headway, but if he takes the matter good-humouredly he is laying the foundation for subsequent harmonious relations, wherein his merits are justly recognized.

It may be well to assert boldly that the inexperienced man is not welcomed in any factory; he gets but little assistance, and must pay the full price for experience, for in the modern factory every individual is fully occupied with his own concerns, and has not the leisure to teach another to avoid mistakes, or to correct the mistakes that are made. This state of affairs is particularly applicable to progress work, for in this connection the junior (and sometimes the senior) posts are filled by an intelligent clerk or labourer, who has not the slightest idea of what progress work is. He is told to chase up details in a certain department, and is at once regarded as a nuisance by the officials of that department. He gets far more kicks than help, for he is always committing blunders—he either goes too far, or not far enough.

With a planning and routeing system, such as the one described in the first portion of this work, each progress man has his duties clearly defined, and the haphazard is eliminated. Each link in the chain of organization has been tested, and proved capable of carrying the load, and efficiency is the result. On the other hand, it must not be forgotten that diversity of manufacture demands greater individuality in the matter of organization, and it is in this connection that "progress work" assumes the highest importance. The ideas given in this work may be applied to any factory engaged upon any class of industry, and worked in conjunction with any existing system. The procedure is essentially British, devised to cater for the requirements of the British manufacturer, with a view to improving efficiency; for until a determined effort is made in this direction, industry will continue to languish, and a return to commercial prosperity will as a consequence be delayed.

INDEX